The Caves of the Great Hunters

How four boys and a dog accidentally discovered the greatest of prehistoric art treasures at Lascaux in southwestern France in 1940, and what they learned about the significance of their find, make a story more captivating than fiction. Along with the boys, the reader also learns of the equally dramatic explorations of other young people to whom the world owes the discovery of the important caves.

The great hunters of the Ice Age have left us, in their extraordinary paintings, a picture of the mighty beasts they hunted and subdued. Many of these marvelous paintings and drawings, made some 20,000 years ago, are reproduced in this book. Together with the story of these caves is also the stirring account of the indomitable spirit of prehistoric man and his struggles for survival.

The **CAVES**

of the **GREAT**

HUNTERS

Hans Baumann

Newly illustrated and revised edition

PANTHEON BOOKS

Translated by Isabel and Florence McHugh

Copyright © 1954 by Pantheon Books Inc.
Revised, authorized translation copyright © 1962 by
Pantheon Books, a Division of Random House, Inc.

Originally published under the title
Die Höhlen der grossen Jäger
© Sigbert Mohn Verlag, Gütersloh 1961

Lascaux photographs by Prof. Dr. Erich Pietsch,
all other color plates by L. and H. Burges
Drawings and maps by Hans Peter Renner
Cover design by Hans Peter Renner after color
photographs from Niaux and Le Portel

Library of Congress Catalog Card Number: 62–15414
Manufactured in the United States of America,
by H. Wolff, New York

Contents

The Where and How 3

Four Boys and a Dog 7

A Teacher Performs an Indian Dance 26

The Abbé Is Not in Paris—But He Comes All the Same 37

The Girl of Altamira 42

The Great Ice Age 49

The Look in the Eye of the Bison 59

The King Visits the Cave 65

The Professors from All Over the World 77

The Artist with the Sealed Mouth 87

An Arrow Speeds over the Valley 105

The River in the Mountain and the Cat's Hole 138

The Cave of the Bison Dances 150

The Mystery of the Bright Hands 161

Stepping Out into Sunshine 173

Epilogue 177

Appendix to the New Edition 179

Europe at the Time of the Great Glaciation 180

Some Caves and Other Sites of Ice Age and Later Ice Age Art 182

Picture Caves Discovered by Girls and Boys 183

The Caves of the Great Hunters

The Where and How

In the south of France the river Dordogne flows down toward the Bay of Biscay. On its banks there are vineyards and almond trees, and slopes covered with fruit trees; and in the ground are truffles. Hills to the north keep off the rough winds. The nearness of the sea assures sufficient rain. On cloudless days, all over that countryside which, like its river, is called Dordogne, there is brilliant light which makes everything distinctly visible. And it makes the inhabitants bright and merry.

In a remote valley of this countryside there are strange houses to be found. They cling to the steep walls of the valley. The overhanging rock forms the back walls of these houses and often their roofs. These human nests cling even halfway up the steep walls of rock. Some of them hide age-old entrances, behind which human beings lived in caves thousands of years ago, at a time when a great part of Europe lay buried under ice.

The dwelling caves of the people of the Ice Age have been searched for remains for about a hundred years now. The archaeologists, digging carefully, have uncovered layer upon layer. At the entrances of many caves they have penetrated more than thirty feet down and brought to light weapons and implements made of flint and of the bones of animals. They have found harpoons, flint scrapers, and bone points. The bones were not only the bones of deer and roe and wild boar, but also those of mammoths, panthers, woolly rhinoceroses, bears, and bison. Many of the objects point to the fact that the people of the Ice Age were great hunters.

The objects found were sent to museums. One of

Fawn, Levanzo; engraved on rock

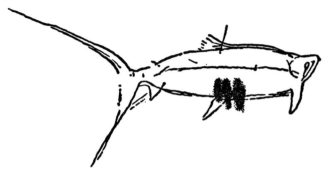

Fish with three red marks, Pindal (outline engraved, marks painted)

the finest collections is in the Dordogne region, in an old castle which, like the peculiar houses already mentioned, is perched high against a rocky wall.

In the course of the last century many caves in which the great hunters dwelt have been discovered. Then one day caves were brought to light in which the great hunters had left behind neither weapons nor implements but in their place something from which their most secret thoughts can be read. They did not dwell in those caves. Only one of their dead remained behind as watchman when they forsook the hunting grounds around the caves.

Mysterious chambers and passages such as those referred to exist not only in Dordogne. Almost a hundred caves of this kind have been found in France and Spain up to the present. Most of them were discovered by cave seekers. But the discoverers also number hunters and peasants, and one *alcalde*, that is, a Spanish mayor.

The most important Ice Age cave of all was discovered by four boys of Montignac, a little village in Dordogne. The four boys are Marcel, George, Jim, and Simon. Marcel and Jim now act as guides to the people from all countries who come to visit the caves. Three gates, the biggest of which is like the doorway of a temple, protect the entrance, to which a broad flight of steps leads down. A motor road has been made. The trees and bushes have been cleared away around the entrance to the cave, and the yellow sandy ground is trodden by thousands of feet.

On September 12, 1940, the day of the discovery, the sparse pine wood which covered this spot was still untouched. Up till then no one apart from the forester and occasionally a few children ever went near the hill which bears the name of Lascaux on maps of the district.

Four Boys and a Dog

In the early afternoon of that September day, Marcel, George, Jim, and Simon wandered through the little oak forest to the south of their village of Montignac and approached the top of the Lascaux hill. This hill, which was timbered with pine trees, was their favorite haunt.

They had a dog with them. His name was Robot and he belonged to Simon, the youngest of the four boys. Simon let Robot run free, even in the wood. The forester had once taken him to task about it. "Now, Simon, haven't you got a leash?" he had asked.

"Yes, I have," Simon admitted.

"Then use it on Robot!"

Simon gave one whistle. Robot came bounding along and didn't leave Simon's side again.

"What if he were to go after a young deer or a hare?" the forester had objected.

"It's a pity you have no hares here," Simon had answered. "It wouldn't make any difference to Robot. My whistle is as good as a leash to him."

The forester had laughed at this. And he had never

again said anything when he met Simon and saw Robot running free in the wood. It was quite unthinkable that Robot would break away or go after the animals.

Hare, Le Gabillou (engraved)

The four boys had no definite aim. They loved to see the trunks of the pine trees glow like copper in the autumn sunshine. It was pleasant to feel the sandy earth softly yielding under their feet at every step. They gazed around them and didn't worry at all about keeping to the path. There was scarcely any underbrush, and plenty of room between the tree trunks. One could see a great distance ahead.

The boys were already past the oaks when Marcel stopped suddenly. He looked around him, then stepped back a few paces and peered about on all sides.

"I can't see Robot any more," he said. "Where is he?"

"He was here just now," said Jim.

"He was hardly ten steps in front of me," said George.

"Wait a sec," said Simon. He whistled.

The four stood listening with attention. Nothing stirred. Simon whistled once more, and his whistle cut through the stillness, then ceased like the drop of a curtain. But Robot did not appear.

"It's not five seconds since I saw him," said Jim.

"Whistle again," said Marcel to Simon.

"It's no good," replied Simon. He looked around helplessly.

"But he can't just have disappeared off the earth!" said George.

"Why not?" asked Marcel. "Perhaps the ground has swallowed him."

"Nonsense!" said Jim, who had noticed how scared little Simon was.

Simon caught George by the arm. "Where did you see him last?" he asked.

George went over to the spot, and the other three followed him. There was only a small shrub there, and no Robot. That was quite obvious. Suddenly Simon knelt down and felt the ground. He had noticed a little hole just under the shrub. Shreds of moss were hanging over it. He tore the moss away and lifted up some stones. Marcel found that the roots of the shrub were in the way, so he took out his knife.

"Don't worry," he said to Simon as he cleared away the earth from under the roots. "He can't be anywhere else but in this hole, and we'll soon get him out."

Marcel kept cutting away quickly. Soon the hole was so big that he could get his head and shoulders inside.

"It really has swallowed him," he said, when he drew out his head again.

"Oh, look at his head!" said George, for Marcel had sand and bits of roots in his hair.

"Didn't you hear anything?" asked Simon. "Robot always barks at once if any of us comes near him."

"The hole goes much farther down," said Marcel. "And it's terribly narrow."

"It would be easier for me to get through," said Simon, and he tried to push Marcel away. But Marcel wouldn't budge from the hole. "Who knows how far down it goes?" he said.

"It's certainly a fox hole or a badger's burrow, and you'll never get into it," said Jim. "And if it is, Robot will surely come back at once."

Two engraved staves with holes in them, the smaller from El Castillo, the larger from Teyjat

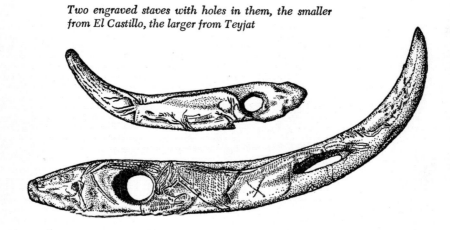

RIGHT: *Galloping horse, Lascaux*

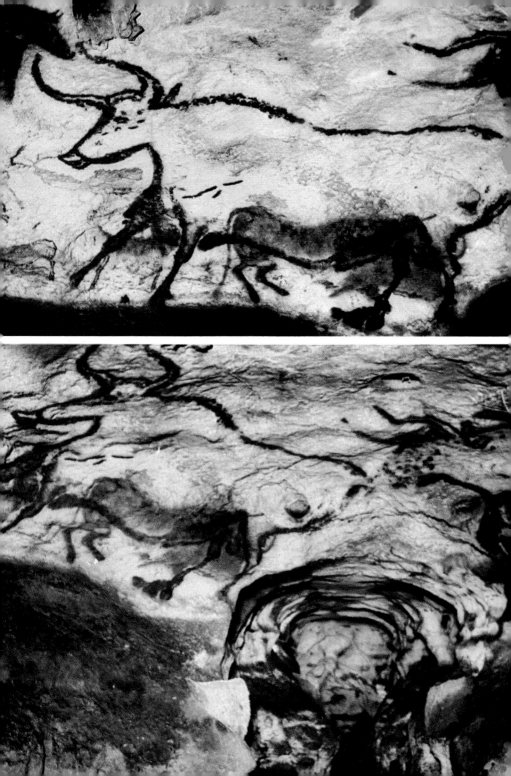

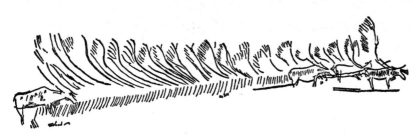

Procession of reindeer (scratched on the bone of an eagle)

They waited. Robot did not come.

"He isn't coming!" exclaimed Simon. "But why isn't he?"

"Perhaps there are several openings," George suggested.

"It's not a fox hole or a badger's burrow," said Marcel. "It's something quite different. And I'll soon find out what it is."

When Simon again tried to push himself in front, Marcel said, "I know already what it is. It's a cave, but there's no way of telling how big it is or how far down it goes. People have often found caves like this. I know what I have to do. Now, this is *my* business."

The others knew that it was no good to oppose him. Whenever there was something risky afoot, no one else had a chance. Marcel saw the reproach in the others' eyes.

"*Our* business," he corrected himself. "But I am responsible for all of you, and also for Robot." Then he began to feel his way head foremost down into the narrow opening, clearing away a few more lumps of earth and some stones with his right hand as he did so.

ABOVE: *Aurochs (primitive oxen) over red cattle, Lascaux*
BELOW: *View into the Long Aisle from the Hall of the Bulls, Lascaux*

"It seems to get wider farther down," he said, as his head disappeared.

"Won't you wait till we get a rope?" asked George. "I can fetch one."

"It gets wider in here—it's already quite comfortable. . . ." came the muffled reply from the hole as Marcel's feet disappeared.

The other three lay on their stomachs with their faces close to the hole. They could hear Marcel dragging himself forward. Suddenly they heard a loud rumbling, and immediately afterward the muffled noise of falling stones. A frightful silence followed.

"It caved in," whispered George.

Jim and Simon tried to say something, but they just couldn't get out a sound. They lay there as if each of them were weighed down by a heavy stone.

"We must get a rope," said George in a husky voice. The three were about to stand up when they heard a faint call coming from the hole: "Robo-o-o——"

And immediately the call was repeated, more faintly and from deeper down in the earth. That is the echo, thought the three. What a big cave it must be!

"He's alive!" cried George. "He's looking for Robot!" And George and Jim called out, "Marcel, Marcel!"

But Simon without a word pushed himself into the hole, and the two others followed behind. For a few yards it was level inside, and then the ground sloped downward. Simon groped before him in the dark. He noticed that the loose earth ceased and that rocks began to appear at each side of him and overhead. He went forward quickly. And just as he emerged into an open space, he bumped squarely into Marcel.

"Why did you stop so suddenly?" asked Simon.

"Do you think I want to break my neck?" Marcel retorted as he stared into the inky-black emptiness that lay beneath him. The stones had now stopped rolling down into the abyss. All was silent.

"Robo-o-o———!" cried Marcel once more.

There wasn't a stir or a sound.

Perhaps he's dead, thought Marcel. But aloud he said, "I'm sure Robot is looking for another opening. He's no fool. But we can't do anything down here without a rope and a light." He began to crawl backward.

With a heavy heart Simon made way for him. They covered the opening carefully, and then considered what they should do next.

"It seems to be a huge cave," remarked Marcel. "It would be crazy to penetrate any deeper without making sure how we'd get out again."

Simon could not stop thinking of Robot. "And when shall we go on searching?" he asked dejectedly.

"Very early in the morning," declared Marcel, who had already worked out a sound plan in his head. "I'll get a rope, and I'll make a reliable lamp for us."

That was just what he did as soon as he got home. The three others looked on baffled as he took a bicycle pump, removed the piston, stopped up the lower of the two holes, filled the casing with oil, and stuck a wick through the hole at the top. The lamp gave a strong even light.

"This won't go out quickly on us," Marcel said confidently. "Who knows how long we shall need to stay down in the cave?"

After a night in which Simon hardly closed an eye, the four set out for the hill of Lascaux armed with a rope and the lamp. On reaching the opening Marcel tied the rope around his waist, and with the lighted lamp in his hand, pushed himself through the entrance. The others crawled cautiously after him, keeping a firm hold on the rope.

When he had crawled in far enough Marcel shone the light ahead into the cave. He saw a roomy chamber that dropped down about twenty-one feet.

"Now hold the rope firmly, all of you!" he shouted back to the others, "and pay it out slowly as I drop down."

To be sure, some stones came loose and tumbled into the depths, but apart from a few scratches, Marcel got down all right. Simon and Jim also reached the floor of the cave successfully with the help of the rope. Then the three made a human ladder for George.

"What a lot of room there is in here!" exclaimed Jim. "It's quite a hall!"

"And none of you is thinking about how I'm to get you up again!" Marcel grumbled.

Simon put his hand over Marcel's mouth. In the silence he whistled. They listened as the whistle echoed from one wall of the cave to the other, until it faded away deep down under the hill. But it was not lost. It found Robot. Robot came running; they could hear his great leaps even before they saw him. He jumped up at Simon so wildly that he almost threw him over. Mad with joy, he danced around the four boys. It was the first time he had broken clean away from them. It was not my fault, Robot tried to assure them with his muzzle, his paws, and his tail. The hole in the ground caught me, the dark space gave way and I slid down—something drew me on and on until the whistle reached me. . . .

"Quiet, Robot," Simon kept repeating. He knelt down by him and stroked his flanks. Robot looked at Simon. The earth simply swallowed me, Robot seemed to say as he looked around at the four. But now we're together again, and all is well.

All isn't so well, Marcel thought. Not a soul knows where we are now. But he didn't say this aloud. He shone the lamp into the high passage out of which

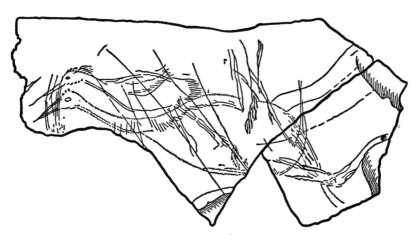

Birds engraved on stone, Labastide

Robot had come back to them. He played the beam over the walls. The ray glided across the roof, from which a broad strip in the center had broken off and lay in pieces on the ground. The walls had sharp edges on top.

It is like being in a ravine, thought Marcel, but with a sky of rock above. There are heavy clouds up there which have never moved—clouds of stone. Ever since they have been there not a breath of wind has touched them, nor a ray of sunshine.

Marcel kept these ideas to himself. The others might be frightened, he thought, if they realized how alone they all were down there. . . .

The light moved over the wall to the left. Who knows if a human being has ever been here before? thought Marcel, because a person can hardly get in through that narrow hole—neither a person nor an animal.

"Look! Horses!" cried Simon. "There are horses here!" He took hold of Marcel's arm, then he took the lamp from him and lit up the place where he saw the horses.

"Nonsense!" said Marcel. "Horses down here?"

"A whole lot of them!" cried Jim.

"And cows and stags!" shouted George.

"Are you all crazy?" asked Marcel. He still did not see anything.

At this Simon shone the light on one place for quite a long time and pointed to the horse's mane and tail and hoofs. And now Marcel too saw it—a horse, a reddish-brown horse. It was quite close to him, near enough to catch. He reached out to the horse. It was not startled, but stayed at the same spot, although it had its forehoof raised ready to jump. The horse felt cold to the touch, and when Marcel looked at his finger, he found that the tip was reddish brown.

"It's paint," he said, "real paint. The horse is painted, but in such a way that anyone would think it's alive! How good that it's paint, something we know about. I thought at first you were all bewitched, and then it seemed to happen to me too. And when I saw the animal I thought that only magic animals could be down here, and I was expecting the magician to appear any minute and say, 'Hello! How nice of you to come and visit me. . . .'"

"Look over there!" cried Simon. "Look at that strange animal! I've never seen such an animal. . . . Look at its long horns as straight as candles."

"Hand that light back, will you!" said Marcel in a hoarse voice. "Must you light up everything?" But he himself flashed the light all over the weird animal—the belly which hung nearly to the ground, the thick head, the horns which stood out from the head like two spears.

This animal was uncanny. Marcel lit up the left wall again, section by section. Above the horse which he had touched was another, and beside that one yet another, and farther up there was one too. And they were all racing in a headlong gallop. Opposite them were stags with mighty antlers, one reddish, another black, another light brown—a whole herd in rapid movement. Beyond them were powerful cattle of huge dimensions with horns longer than a man's arm.

The boys went farther into the cave. It became narrower and the ground sloped. The steep walls were completely covered with large animals, and above, where the walls formed a vaulted roof, there were cows with long necks and narrow heads. Many of the pictures were only drawn in outline, while others were fully painted in color. And then there were pictures painted over pictures which still could be seen.

To the left, in the narrow passage, the boys saw a big black bull with angry flaming eyes.

"It's raging!" cried Simon. "Why is it so angry?"

Marcel pointed to one of the bull's front legs, toward which something dark was flying.

"Perhaps it's an arrow," said Marcel.

"But where's the hunter?" asked Jim.

The boys looked around, but there was no hunter to be seen anywhere. Right at the back they discovered a horse plunging backward over a precipice. And suddenly Simon pointed to the wall on the right and cried, "Ponies! Look, ponies! How merrily they're trotting!"

"A whole row of ponies! And look, over there above them, there's a cow running toward a fence—or perhaps it's a manger," cried George.

The boys turned back to the wide gallery with the giant cattle. A passage branched off at the side. Here they saw smaller animals—ibex, horses, and, where the passage became somewhat wider, an enormous cow. Then they came upon two huge animals. The back half of their bodies looked like that of a bull, but the front half was much heavier. Both of them were black, and one of them had a fiery red stripe across its body. Their huge necks were bent threateningly, their front feet thrown forward. They were fighting beasts who had turned their backs on each other for a moment in order to gather force for a fresh onslaught.

Simon was beginning to feel frightened. He turned around and examined the other side of the passage. There he saw stags—a whole herd of them—but only

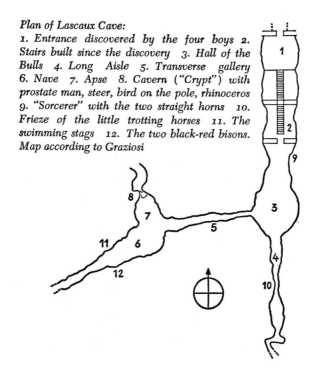

Plan of Lascaux Cave:
1. Entrance discovered by the four boys 2. Stairs built since the discovery 3. Hall of the Bulls 4. Long Aisle 5. Transverse gallery 6. Nave 7. Apse 8. Cavern ("Crypt") with prostate man, steer, bird on the pole, rhinoceros 9. "Sorcerer" with the two straight horns 10. Frieze of the little trotting horses 11. The swimming stags 12. The two black-red bisons. Map according to Graziosi

their heads, which were all stretched out.

"They look like that when they're swimming," said Marcel after a while. "And look, there's the river!"

He pointed to the dark strip from which the slender necks of the stags emerged.

"Oh, yes," said Jim. "The front one is standing up. He's just getting out of the water."

A short passage branched off sideways. The boys did not notice anything special in it. But suddenly they found themselves in front of a big shaft. Marcel shone his light into it. The ground sloped steeply downward for several yards. Marcel said, "I'll let myself down there on the rope."

He slid down and lighted up the walls of this crypt. He pretended there was nothing to be seen, but he noticed at once that there was a man there. The man was lying with his arms stretched out as if he had fallen backward. Over the man stood one of the wild animals that looked half like a bull. The animal was raging. Its belly was torn open by a spear; its head was lowered, ready to attack. The horns were pointing to

Man with bird mask, bird on the pole, wounded bison, and rhinoceros,
"Crypt," Lascaux

the man who was lying there before it.

"Do you see anything?" Jim called down the shaft.

"No, nothing," replied Marcel, lighting up the empty spaces on the wall.

"No ponies?" asked Simon.

"Nothing," repeated Marcel. And he thought to himself: Simon mustn't see this man with the furious bull standing over him. . . .

He took the lamp and began climbing up. Jim and Simon stretched down to help him.

"It's funny that there are only animals down here," remarked Jim and George, as they all walked back.

"Yes," said Marcel, "nothing but animals."

"But the animal right in front, with the hanging

21

belly and the straight horns," said Jim. "What a strange animal that is! Its legs are just like a man's."

Marcel did not answer. He was thinking of the man down there in the crypt.

"The stags are the most beautiful of all the animals," said George, and Marcel agreed.

"What about the ponies?" Simon piped up. "You've forgotten the ponies!"

"The ponies are pretty wonderful," admitted Jim.

"What kind of animals are those that have one half like bulls?"

"And that animal with the straight horns?"

They were now back again in the first part of the cave. Robot rubbed against Simon's knees. He wanted to get up into the light. They all wanted to get out.

"We could ask my teacher, Mr. Laval," suggested Simon. "He once told us about caves where people used to live."

Jim looked at Marcel. "But the cave is *our* secret," he said.

"We must go and tell him about it all the same," Marcel decided after a little hesitation. "This cave must certainly be very important. Did you ever hear of a cave with pictures painted on the walls?"

"Who can have painted them?" asked Simon.

"The man must be dead long ago," said Marcel.

"But the paint is still quite fresh!"

"That's true," said Marcel. "But the cave was almost competely sealed up. Perhaps Mr. Laval can explain it all to us. I know he's interested in caves."

"But it must remain *our* cave," said Jim. "It was Robot and we who found it."

"My teacher can be trusted," Simon assured them.

I could also ask him about the man who's lying down there, thought Marcel to himself. Aloud he said, "The day after tomorrow we'll tell him about it. But for tomorrow the cave must belong to us alone. No one except . . ." He stopped short.

"Except who?" asked George.

"Except just ourselves," said Marcel.

With the loose stones that lay in the middle of the first chamber they built themselves makeshift stairs, and then climbed out, Robot trotting in front. They all breathed a sigh of relief as soon as they were once more in the open air, where there were trees and sunshine.

The next day they brought the rope again, and besides each one brought a flashlight. They could now see the pictures much more clearly than the day before. In the short passage that led to the shaft they discovered smaller pictures, which were engraved in the rock. Marcel tried to stop the others from turning their lights into the cryptlike pit at the bottom of the shaft, but he couldn't.

George was the first to go down. Jim and Simon also got down safely. Only a flashlight was broken. Marcel remained above with Robot.

Jim was the first to see the man who was lying there on his back with outstretched arms. And the three of them saw the raging animal.

"Didn't you see this yesterday?" Jim called up to Marcel.

"Yes, I saw it," said Marcel.

"And why did you keep it from us?"

"Because it's not good for you to see," declared Marcel firmly.

Robot began to whine as Marcel let himself down.

"The animal's belly has been torn open by a spear, and the guts are hanging out," said Simon suddenly.

"That's right," said Marcel. "Come, let us climb up again!"

"What a strange bird over there on the pole!" cried Jim.

"And look how the man is painted," said George. "Just with a few strokes—quite different from the animal!"

"The man has a bird's head!" cried Simon.

"I dreamed about that last night," Marcel confessed.

"The spear has killed the animal," said George, "but the man must have fallen before it did. Look how he's lying there! He has fainted!"

"Looks like it," said Marcel. "Now, let's go!"

"There's another animal over there," said Jim.

Marcel looked closely. The forelegs were missing, but the back, hind legs, and tail were all there, and the animal had two horns sticking out from its nose, the back one being only half the length of the front one.

"That can't be anything but a rhinoceros," said Marcel. "But there aren't any rhinoceroses in France; at least they're only in the Zoo!"

They continued searching and found a horse in a

recess. Then their eyes were again drawn to the man and the raging animal.

"Why is the bird there on the pole?" asked Simon, looking up at Marcel.

"Perhaps your teacher can tell us that too," said Marcel. "And it's best if we go to him at once."

"Why so quickly?" asked the other three.

"Do you also want to dream about it tonight?"

Robot began to whine again. Then they climbed out and went straight to Simon's teacher, for they knew that he was eager to hear about caves.

A Teacher Performs an Indian Dance

The boys saw Mr. Léon Laval going up to his house. He was wearing a beret. He was never seen out of doors without his beret. Mr. Laval was well over fifty, and he was very strict in school. But his pupils liked him because he was fair and still more because it was never boring in any of his classes. Marcel gave Simon a questioning look.

"How do you get on—in school, I mean?" he asked.

"All right," said Simon.

"Then you'd best go up to him alone."

"But not without Robot!"

Mr. Laval was somewhat surprised at Simon's visit, especially as he arrived with the dog.

"He was there," Simon explained eagerly.

"Where?" asked Mr. Laval.

"He was really the first into the cave," said Simon. "We would never have found it without him. But of course it was *we*," he continued, "who noticed the animals. Robot didn't see them, or at least I don't think he did."

"What animals?" asked the teacher. Simon could see

ABOVE: *Swimming stags, Lascaux*
BELOW: *Fighting bison, Lascaux*

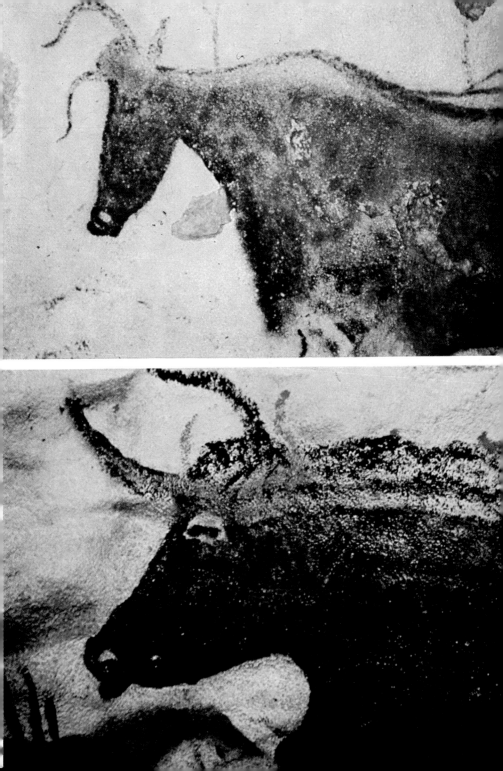

that he was looking uneasily, now at Robot, now at him.

"The horses," said Simon. "We saw the horses first. On the wall to the left, when Marcel shone his light on it. *I* saw them, sir, and then George and Jim saw the cows and the stags. Marcel thought first we were crazy, but then *he* saw the reddish-brown horse, and he touched it and got paint on his fingertip."

Mr. Laval stood up. "Where did you see the horses and stags and cows?" he asked excitedly.

"In the cave," said Simon. "Up there on the Lascaux hill, in the pine wood that belongs to Count La Rochefoucauld. Robot had suddenly disappeared into a hole in the ground, and we wanted to help him to get out. Marcel crawled down into a pit. . . . Say, Mr. Laval, what kind of animals are those that are half like bulls, but the front half of them much wilder looking? Do you know those animals?"

Mr. Laval went up to a desk, opened a drawer quickly, and took a few magazines out of it. Simon noticed that his hands were trembling as he looked through the papers. Simon could see pictures of horses, like the ones that were painted in the cave, with tangled manes that stood on end. And then the teacher pointed to a picture and asked, "Are the animals like that?"

"Yes," said Simon. "What kind of animals are they?"

Mr. Laval looked at Simon searchingly. "Are they really animals like these?" he asked.

"They're exactly like those," said Simon, very positively. "But they're especially wild ones, and one of

ABOVE: *Cow from the Long Aisle, Lascaux*
BELOW: *Head of the big black bull, Lascaux*

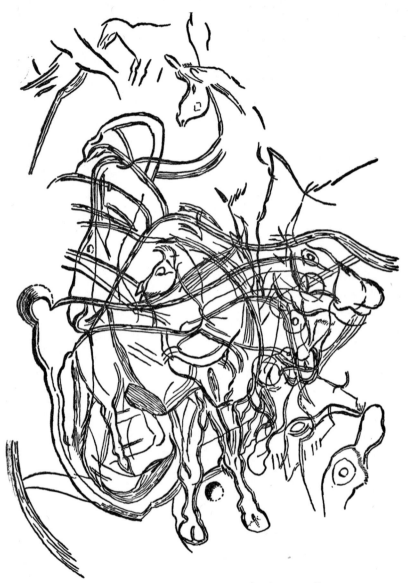

Various animals, especially horses, Pair-non-Pair (engraved)

them has its belly torn open by a spear, and there's a man lying in front of its horns. What kind of animals are they?"

Instead of replying Mr. Laval did something which astounded Simon. Probably a teacher had never before done such a thing with a pupil. With both hands he took hold of Simon, clasped him tight, kissed him on both cheeks, and then swung him around and around until Simon was quite dizzy. While he was doing this, noises such as Simon had never heard before and could never have imagined possible from him, of all people, came out of the teacher's mouth. His actions were what Simon imagined a Red Indian dance would be like.

"But what on earth is wrong with you, Mr. Laval?" he cried as soon as he was released.

"I'm off my head!" cried Mr. Laval, "I'm mad with joy! You don't know yet what you have discovered!"

"Is it the animals?" asked Simon timidly. "What kind of animals are they, really?"

Mr. Laval pulled himself together. "They're bison," he said, beaming with joy as if bison were the most lovable animals in the world. "Without a doubt they're bison. You have found a cave with paintings in it which are at least a thousand times as old as you are."

He's really off his head, thought Simon.

"I must see them at once!" said Mr. Laval.

"But perhaps you won't be able to get through," remarked Simon dubiously. "The hole is very narrow."

"I'll get through," declared the teacher, "even if I have to become a mole to do so!"

29

Simon had never seen his teacher like this; he seemed suddenly about twenty years younger. He strode rapidly out of the house.

Out on the street he beckoned the three other boys. "Let's be off!" he said. The boys stared at him.

"Why are you staring at me like that?" asked Mr. Laval. "Am I a ghost?"

"No, Mr. Laval," said Marcel. "But, your beret . . ."

Mr. Laval grasped his head. For the first time he had left the house without his beret. But Simon was already racing back to the house for it, with Robot at his heels.

Mr. Laval walked very quickly, although it was uphill all the way. He did not speak a word. When they got to the entrance, it was not easy for him to get in. But that didn't stop him. He tore away the stones and lumps of earth. When the boys wanted to help him, he would not let them.

"Mr. Laval!" said Marcel when the opening was big enough and the teacher wanted to push his head into the hole.

"What is it?" asked the teacher irritably.

"Shouldn't we post sentries?" Marcel made a sign to George and Jim, while he pointed to Robot.

"Do what you like," said Mr. Laval, crawling into the hole.

"Mr. Laval!" cried Marcel again. But the teacher continued to crawl in. Then all four of them caught him by the legs and pulled him out again.

"What's the matter now?" asked Mr. Laval crossly.

"We can't let you go down like that," said Marcel.

"You can't see a thing without a light. Please let me go in first to light the way for you. It's dangerous—the shaft . . ."

Mr. Laval admitted this. So Marcel crawled in first, then the teacher followed, with Simon on his heels. George and Jim kept Robot up above. The three stood guard to see that no other person should approach too close to the entrance that was opening wider and wider on the hill of Lascaux.

When Mr. Laval saw the first pictures he took off his beret. Even now down in the cave he didn't speak a word but went on searching from picture to picture. Simon noticed that at sight of many of the pictures the teacher's face twitched. Obviously he was trying to speak, but no words would come. When he looked up at the ceiling, with its many pictures of aurochs, one after another, his beret dropped from his hand without his noticing it. Only when they were all out-side once more, and had already closed up the en-trance with stones, did the boys notice that the beret was missing for the second time.

"Never mind," said Mr. Laval to Marcel, who wanted to go back and fetch it. "I have another one at home."

"But, Mr. Laval, people will notice it if you're bare-headed," said Simon. "And your coat and trousers are quite dirty. People will ask what's the matter."

Mr. Laval beat the dirt off his clothes as best he could. "Not a word out of you!" he said sternly.

"Not a word!" Marcel assured him. The others nodded agreement.

31

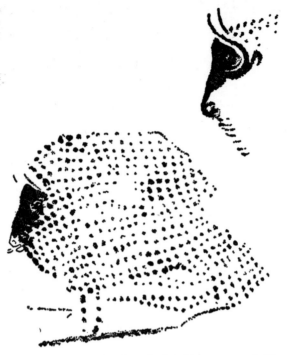

Two spotted bison, head of the left bison engraved, Marsoulas

"Excellent!" said Mr. Laval, as if he were giving marks in class.

"And what about Count La Rochefoucauld, to whom the hill of Lascaux belongs?" asked Jim.

"Naturally he must be told about it," said Mr. Laval. "And I'm quite certain he'll realize the importance of the cave right away, and admire you for discovering it so cleverly." But seeing the look of disappointment on the faces of the four boys, he continued with a wink, "But not today or tomorrow. For a few days more the cave shall belong to you four boys, and no one else shall know about the pictures except myself and . . ."

"Then, there is someone else?" interrupted Marcel anxiously.

"It can't be helped if you want to learn all about the bison, and the man lying on his back, and the animal with the straight horns."

"We *do* want to know," said little Simon. "But surely *you* could tell us all about them. You've books and magazines with pictures of them! And you knew right away what I was talking about when I'd hardly said two words about the cave!"

Mr. Laval shook his head. "What would you say,"

Hunter with animal mask,
Racó Molero, Gasulla Gorge

he said, "if I were to bring the man who knows more than anyone else in the world about such cave pictures and the artists who painted them? The man who can really put you in the picture about how people lived twenty thousand years ago? Who can tell you how they overcame the dangers that beset them on all sides, how they defended themselves, and the weapons they used to fight the bison and other mighty animals which contended with them for the hunting grounds? I'm convinced that there's not another man in the world as expert in reading traces thousands of years old as the man I have in mind. And perhaps he may even be able to tell you what moved those painters, who are the earliest artists we know about, to seek out dark caves and paint pictures in them—on naked rock."

Mr. Laval lowered his voice. "You will learn from him what people thought back in those days, thousands of years ago," he said.

"How can that be?" asked George. "After all, thoughts last only a minute, and then they're gone and nothing is left of them."

Mr. Laval stared before him for a moment, lost in thought, then he continued in the same quiet voice: "That's not so with *all* thoughts. There are thoughts that become deeds—deeds that are spoken of for many a day. And there are thoughts that turn into pictures—then time cannot destroy them so easily. After many, many years a practiced eye can still read these thoughts from the colors and lines of the pictures. Naturally these pictures cannot say very much to *us* because they are the first cave pictures any of us has ever seen. But the man whom I'm going to inform of your discovery has been examining caves for years and years. In many of these caves he has worked under the most difficult conditions; for months he worked, lying on his back for eight hours a day, day in and day out, copying cave pictures onto big sheets of paper."

"You know the man personally, then?" asked Jim.

"No, only from books and magazines," explained Mr. Laval. "He's the great archaeologist Henri Breuil. He lives in Paris and he's an Abbé."

"An Abbé?" exclaimed Simon. The three others looked incredulous too.

"Yes," continued Mr. Laval, "Henri Breuil is a priest, and he's one of the most famous scholars in all France. He can tell you everything you want to know about caves. And he will do so, I know, because you boys have made a discovery which is as important as the discovery of America—or almost. But now let me hurry off to the post office to send a telegram."

"Wait a minute!" cried George, as Mr. Laval was turning away.

"What is it now?" asked the teacher impatiently.

"What if the post office lets out something?"

"The post is confidential," said Simon, proud of his knowledge.

"And will the Abbé really come, even from Paris?"

"He will come as soon as he possibly can," Mr. Laval assured them. "A telegram doesn't take long to reach Paris."

Simon counted up. "Then the Abbé from Paris will be the seventh to know the secret."

"No, the sixth," his teacher ventured a correction.

"But what about Robot?" asked Simon indignantly.

The Abbé Is Not in Paris—
But He Comes All the Same

In the days following, the boys had many disagreements. George was all for keeping constant watch at the entrance to the cave. He thought at least one of them should have an eye on it all the time, hiding in a bush.

"I'm against it," declared Marcel.

"So am I," said Jim.

"But why?" asked George.

"It would just make people curious," said Marcel.

George was annoyed. Little Simon tried to calm him: "After all, for ten thousand years no one has taken any notice of the cave."

The next day George came along with a new worry. "But if those pictures are really so terribly valuable that a famous man is coming specially from Paris to see them . . . ?" he asked.

"They *are* terribly valuable," replied Marcel. "Mr. Laval doesn't joke."

Simon put in his word. "When *we* discover something," he said, "you can be sure it's something good."

"Have you any doubts about it?" asked Jim.

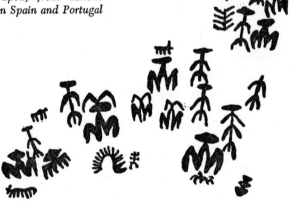

Drawings of abstract figures and demon, freely grouped, from various prehistoric sites in Spain and Portugal

"That's not my worry," replied George. "But if they are so valuable I don't think we should have told Mr. Laval about them."

"And now someone else is to know," said Marcel, amused.

George looked worried indeed. "Have you ever heard of museums?" he asked. "Don't you know that everything of great value is carted off to museums? Once a learned man from Paris comes here and writes about our cave, and makes the pictures known all over the world, the heads of museums will come too, and then . . . I think it looks bad for *our* pictures."

"I don't think so," said Simon. "You're forgetting that those pictures aren't painted on canvas or wood, but on solid rock."

George seemed relieved at this statement.

When Mr. Laval heard of these misgivings, he re-assured George completely. Nobody, he told him, knew better than the Abbé from Paris what should be done to protect the pictures.

The Abbé did not come until the twenty-first of September, nine full days after the discovery. The telegram had not reached him in Paris, but in Brive. He arrived in Montignac in the car of a doctor, a friend of his. When he got out of the car at Mr. Laval's house the four boys were there to meet him. He had announced his arrival by telegram.

"Here are the discoverers," said Mr. Laval, presenting the boys. And the lanky Abbé beamed and shook hands with each of them. Only then did they notice that he was considerably older than Mr. Laval. Mr. Laval wanted him to come into his house straight away for a meal.

"No, Mr. Laval," said the Abbé from Paris, "but thank you very much all the same. We shall eat later. If I took a meal now I might not be able to get through the entrance hole. Sometimes these entrances are not very wide. . . . Besides, I can hardly bear to wait any longer. And you," he continued, looking at the boys, "aren't you going to take me there?"

Marcel and Jim went on ahead, carrying in turn the Abbé's suitcase, which contained denim overalls such as miners wear, a few implements, and a lamp. Mr. Laval walked on the left of the Abbé. George and Simon followed at a respectful distance.

"Isn't he great?" whispered Simon.

"You can tell at once by his eyes that he knows a lot," whispered George. "We'll hear everything now; and I'm sure he'll know what the bird on the pole is doing there too."

"And what kind of horses those are," said Simon. "Because the horses in the cave are different from our horses. And I'm sure he knows all about bison, too, and about that queer animal with horns sticking out from its head like spears."

"Keep quiet," said George. "He's talking to Mr. Laval now."

The two hurried up near the Abbé in order not to miss a word. But the Abbé was only asking whether there were colored pictures in the cave too or only drawings in black. When the teacher had informed him, the Abbé called Marcel and got him to describe the discovery.

When the stones had been cleared away from the mouth of the hole, Mr. Laval said, somewhat hesitantly, "I think it would be a good thing if someone stood guard outside."

The Abbé looked at each of the boys in turn.

But then Mr. Laval declared, "Of course it must not be one of the boys. *They* have discovered the cave, and it's their right to go in first."

"Bravo!" cried Marcel. Too late he realized that he had thought aloud. But it was easy to see that the three others also admired the teacher for his decision.

"But we may be a long time," said the Abbé, taking the overalls out of his suitcase and slipping into them. "One never can tell from the outside."

Marcel came forward with a suggestion. "But the cave need not be left open," he said. "You can camouflage the entrance with a few stones, and we can push them away from the inside."

"That's right. We may be quite a time down there," repeated the Abbé. So Mr. Laval put a few stones in front of the entrance after the Abbé and the four boys had disappeared into the cave.

The Girl of Altamira

Now the young discoverers were alone in their cave with the Abbé from Paris. They led him from picture to picture. At each new picture they hoped that he would begin to explain things to them. He had no difficulty seeing the pictures immediately, and he was now observing them quietly one after the other. And his silence made the silence of the cave seem even deeper. The boys felt this silence grow and grow.

The Abbé stood longest of all in front of the prostrate man with the bird, and the mortally wounded bison. Even down there in the crypt he still said nothing. But when they had climbed up again to the main hall where most of the pictures were, the Abbé sat down on a stone and motioned the boys to sit down too. Then he said, "This cave of yours is not the first one which has been found. But it is the most beautiful one in the whole of France, and it is probably the most magnificent picture cave in the whole world."

The boys held their lights very quietly. The circles of light remained focused on the ceiling, so that the

ABOVE: *Small wild horse, Lascaux*
BELOW: *The animal with the two straight horns, Lascaux*

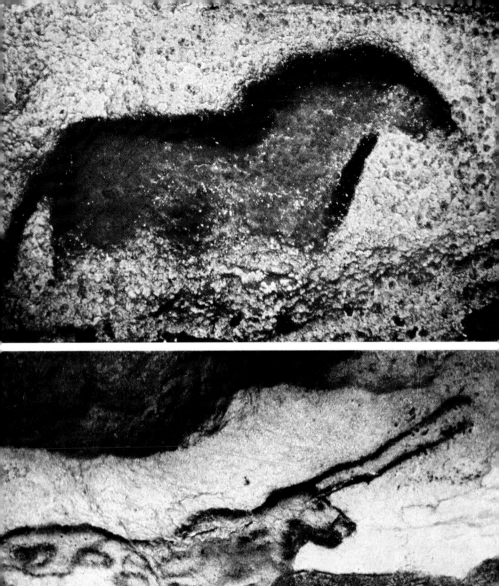

whole space was filled with a faint, even light. And they could see the Abbé quite well.

There he sits like a king, thought Simon; a king who has his kingdom under the earth; and we are his knights, who have won him a new province.

"Have a lot of caves been discovered already?" asked Marcel anxiously. "Caves with pictures too?"

"Nearly ninety up to the present," declared the Abbé reluctantly.

"But ours is surely the first which has been discovered by boys," said Marcel quickly. The big number did not please him at all.

The Abbé did not reply at once.

"Even if ours wasn't the *very* first to be discovered by boys," said Simon in a small voice, "that doesn't matter much."

"Well then, I may as well admit to you that there is *one* cave which is actually named after three boys. It's called '*Trois Frères*'—Three Brothers—because it was discovered by the three sons of Count Bégouën, a great scholar, in the year 1914."

This revelation didn't particularly appeal to the boys. They looked over their knees down at the ground.

"Now, now," said the Abbé, "why get so glum all of a sudden? The three brothers discovered the cave for you also. If you like, I shall ask the Count, to whom the cave belongs, to allow you to visit it some time. It is only very rarely that he lets anyone enter it."

The boys were enthusiastic at the prospect.

ABOVE: *Left-hand wall frieze in the Hall of the Bulls, Lascaux*
BELOW: *Frieze of the little trotting horses, Lascaux*

Engraved animal group (ibex, reindeer, mammoths, aurochs), La Mouthe

The Abbé continued with emphasis: "The fact that other boys before you had the same good luck does not make *your* cave less important."

"How about the other caves?" said Marcel. "Surely those brothers were at least the *first* boys to discover a cave?"

"I'd like to let you think that, since it seems to matter so much to you," said the Abbé, smiling. "But actually, the three sons of the Count were not the first boys. Way back in 1895, four peasant boys penetrated the cave of La Mouthe, which is not very far from

Mammoths from Pech-Merle (above right, painted). The three below from Les Combarelles and Font-de-Gaume (engraved)

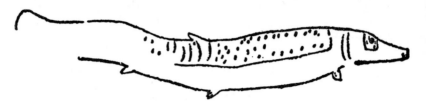

Fish from the Horse Frieze of Pech-Merle (painted)

Lascaux here. The entrance of the La Mouthe Cave
had been blocked for years by the masonry wall of a
barn which had been built under the overhanging rock
like so many houses in that neighborhood. On the
eleventh of April, the four boys, carrying candles, ventured in through a hole in the barn wall. The leader's
name was Gaston. Having penetrated some distance
with difficulty, he had sat down to rest, when suddenly
he saw a picture of a bison on the face of the rock. In
an instant all his tiredness had vanished. He looked
around him and discovered more and more rock pictures—bison, ibex, horses—which were partly covered by a layer of stalactite. A well-known archaeologist named Rivière was informed. He found more
pictures and, in addition, a beautiful lamp with an ibex
engraved on it. Doubtless this lamp had once given
light to the Ice Age hunters, perhaps even to the
painters of the pictures which the four boys discovered in La Mouthe."

"It *would* be four boys!" said Simon, dejectedly. The
others looked disappointed too.

The Abbé tried to cheer them up. "Being the first—
that's not really what matters." he said. "It even hap-

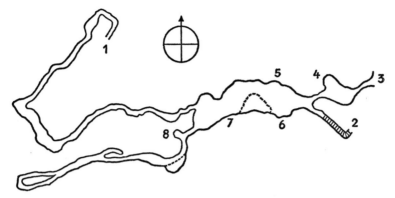

Plan of Pech-Merle Cave: 1. Natural entrance 2. Artificially made entrance with steps 3. Entrance to the recently discovered gallery 4. Scratched drawings on clay 5. Horse frieze (panel) with hands and red fish 6. "Chapel" of the Mammoths 7. Hall with scratchings on clay 8. Human footprints (according to Graziosi)

pened once that a boy led an Abbé into a cave. That Abbé's name was Lemozi, and he was a prehistorian who, like me, studied the Ice Age period. The name of the boy who discovered that cave was David. On February 15, 1920, he succeeded in climbing down into an unusually difficult subterranean passage which led into the hill of Pech-Merle, not far from Cabrerets. Again and again David forced his way into this cave, but not until September 4, 1922, did he reach a distant subterranean hall some 155 yards long, which led into an even larger hall which he found the next day. Both rooms had exciting pictures and signs on their walls. That was almost twenty years ago.

"But long before David, Gaston, and the three brothers, a girl had discovered cave paintings—the first cave paintings ever found. And some of the pictures in that cave are perhaps even more magnificent than the best here in Lascaux. Altamira is the name of that cave. It is in Spain, on the north coast, near Santillana, a township which consists mostly of old palaces."

"And how old was the girl of Altamira?" asked Simon, who still cherished a secret hope that he was the youngest of all cave discoverers.

"She was nine," said the Abbé quietly.

With a timid voice Simon asked, "And what was the girl's name?"

"Maria," said the Abbé. "Forty years ago she herself told me all about that first discovery. And it had taken place about thirty years before that. The girl and her father, who was a nobleman, a Spanish don, had to fight many years for their cave."

The boys were speechless with astonishment at this.

"Yes," said the Abbé, "the discovery itself was only a small part of the story of Altamira. Perhaps this story is the best thing I can give you, better than a few stone implements."

The Abbé from Paris had all the lights switched off except Marcel's. Through its faint light the animals looked down on the boys and the priest.

Then he began to tell the story.

The Great Ice Age

"It is strange," began the Abbé, "that in Altamira too it all began with a dog. Like Robot, he had suddenly disappeared from the earth. The dog belonged to the head gamekeeper of Don Marcelino de Sautuola, whose castle stood near Altamira, in the village of Puente San Miguel. The dog disappeared right in the middle of a meadow which stretched up a gently sloping hillside. The gamekeeper whistled, but his dog didn't come back to him. The gamekeeper searched and found a hole. He began to dig, because he saw at once that it was a hole which neither a fox nor any other animal had made. The dog came up to him out of a cave. Naturally the gamekeeper at once reported the cave under the meadow to Don Marcelino. Don Marcelino went to inspect it. In places the cave was so low that a man could not stand up straight, and he had to take care not to knock his head against the many projections of rock that stuck out from the ceiling of the cave. Neither the Don nor his gamekeeper saw anything special.

"It's just a cave like many others, thought Don

Mammoth, Les Combarelles (engraved)

Marcelino. The only thing that's queer about it is that it's on a low flat hillside. For caves are generally found in mountains, where there are deep ravines.

"For some time no one bothered about the cave. It remained open, but no one entered it.

"Nine years later, in the year of 1878, Don Marcelino went to Paris. A world's fair was being held there. All the things which had been invented or discovered up to that time were on exhibit.

"In one of the halls there were glass cases containing all kinds of objects made of stone or bone. There were knives, awls, scrapers and hammers, spearheads and stone axes—handy weapons which could deliver mighty blows. There were also harpoon points the length of an arm, and bone needles no longer than one's little finger, with fine holes in them like those of the needles with which we sew today. But especially interesting were the stones and pieces of bone on which animals—bison, for example—were engraved."

"And were there ponies too?" asked Simon.

"Yes, there were ponies too," said the Abbé. "One could see clearly that the horses were not the kind we have in our stables. They were wild horses with manes standing on end. To this day there are wild horses like that in Siberia; they are called tarpans. And the animal whose picture is most often scratched on bones and stones—the mammoth—has also been found in Siberia, frozen into the ice, which had preserved it for many thousands of years. It was a giant elephant with a shaggy coat."

"I thought," interrupted George, "that elephants lived only in hot countries."

"No, there were mammoths which could stand the cold, because they wore thick fur coats," explained the Abbé. "There were also rhinoceroses—woolly rhinoceroses—which wore warm winter coats, and they had a thick armor under their fur and two horns on their nose. The front one was over a yard long. And they were certainly very dangerous animals. There were also reindeer, arctic foxes, and snow owls—in fact, all the animals which like cold regions."

"And were these animals also in France long ago?" asked Marcel.

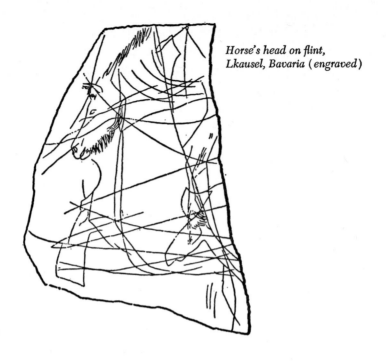

Horse's head on flint,
Lkausel, Bavaria (engraved)

"In France, and also in Spain, and Italy, and Germany. Everywhere in Europe, not only in northern Europe as now, there were reindeer. For at the time that these drawings were scratched on the bones, it was cold in the whole of Europe. That time is called the Ice Age or Glacial Period. The mountains of Norway, the Alps, and the Pyrenees were much higher than they are today. They had two floors, so to speak. The upper floor consisted of ice. Over the dark mountains of rock towered mountains of ice. They shone coldly, and icy streams flowed down from them on all sides. Men and beasts fled from them terrified. Even the very plants fled. Whole woods took flight.

"Naturally, all this happened very slowly, but in the course of decades and decades the ice won more ground and the plants had to content themselves with the little crevices between rocks and ice. Finally, the only plants left were those which even today we find on the edges of the great ice fields—dwarf birches and willows, saxifrages, mosses, and heaths, and, peeping very timidly between wool grass and reeds, occasional flowers—pale poppies, polar carnations, sorrel, ragged robin, and here and there little daisies and violets. People in those days had a hard time; it was no paradise in which they lived. There must have been frightful storms too, with snow in winter, and in summer huge yellow clouds which raced over the earth, destroying and smothering everything. These clouds were formed from the dust of the great steppes which must have existed in those days.

"There were many kinds of animals, not all of them dangerous—for instance, badgers, deer and elk, steppe asses, dwarf hares hardly bigger than rats, reindeer, marmots, shrews, moor owls, buzzards and vultures, muskrats, and duck. In the rivers there were perch and pike. There were also snow hares, Arctic foxes, ermines, antelopes and chamois, lemmings, and wolverines. But many of the other animals which man encountered were his bitter rivals for possession of the part of the earth which the ice left free. There were bears and cave lions, panthers and hyenas, musk oxen, boars, and lynxes. I have already told you about the bison, the mammoth, and the woolly rhinoceros. Man

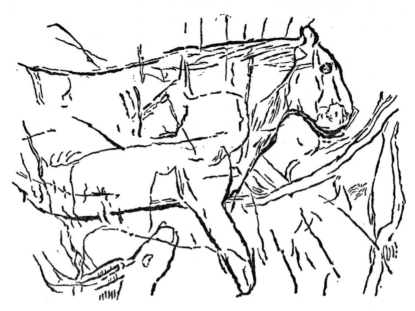

Lioness and other animals' heads, Les Combarelles (engraved)

was unable to avoid these animals. He came upon
them if he took refuge in a cave. He needed meat if he
was not to die of hunger, and skins if he was not to
freeze to death. He had nothing but the bones of these
animals and stone with which to fashion weapons and
tools. And the places where there was shelter from
snow and rain must have been bitterly disputed between man and beast. The learned men who had
found most of the tools and drawings which were ex-
hibited in Paris told the father of the girl of Altamira
that in many caves the bones of bears and of human
beings lay side by side—no one could say which party

had won the fight. Perhaps both had fallen in the struggle.

"During the exhibition Don Marcelino went day after day to the glass cases. From these cases ages long past looked out at him. From the tools and drawings it was plain to see that there must have been several Ice Ages. But the spans of time these epochs represent can only be determined approximately.

"It is thought that the last Ice Age came to an end approximately ten thousand years before Christ. The melting snows carried down deposits of loose stone. From the size of these layers it is possible to calculate their age. Some things at least are known for certain about the close of that last Ice Age, from which come the great colored cave pictures. For instance, the animals which lived at that time are known to us without exception.

"When Don Marcelino looked at a harpoon, he saw before his eyes a bison. All the things which were shown in the other halls seemed to him of little importance when he thought of the courage to which these simple tools and weapons of stone and bone bore witness—of the valor of the hunters who dwelt amid the great ice. Their hands had to be quicker than the claws of a tiger, their minds more alert than all the instincts of the beasts. They had only one helper to banish the wild beasts from their vicinity, one that was even stronger than the ice. But man had to win this helper anew every time he needed it. It was fire. Fireplaces have been found in numerous caves, and many drawings have been found burned on bones by the people of that time. Fire, which man snatched from the glow of the sun and from lightning, and the look which came forth like lightning from the eye of the hunter and met the beast even before the weapon hit it—these were the two things which made prehistoric man stronger than the beasts.

"It was a world of unbroken freedom, in which there were no frontiers as yet, and no clearly defined fields. In spite of the savage beasts, the ice, and the terrible storms that darkened the heavens, it was a paradise for hunters.

"Don Marcelino came home from Paris fired with the desire to learn more about those people, to get nearer to them, and to unearth a trace of them himself. A dazzling gleam from the great ice had entered into his soul.

"Back in Spain, he began visiting the hill of Altamira again and again. He had no difficulty finding the cave. In the ten years which had passed since its discovery the entrance had not changed."

"And had no one entered the cave during all those years?" asked Marcel.

"A few children, yes," said the Abbé, "but then their parents forbade them to go into the cave again."

"Why?" asked Simon. "Were they afraid that the cave would collapse?"

"Or can you get lost in the underground passages?" inquired Jim.

"There are passages which get narrower and lower as you go along," explained the Abbé. "Besides, the

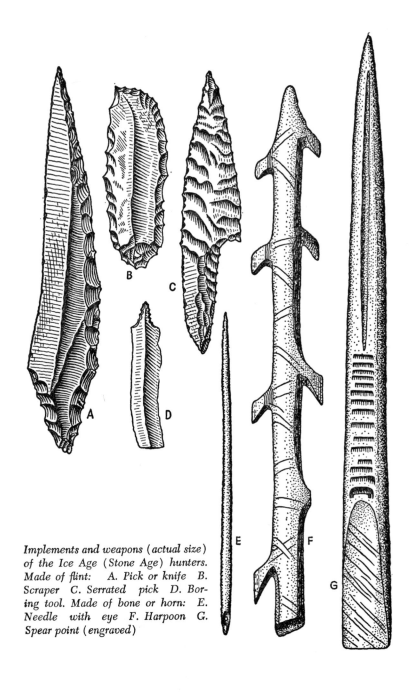

*Implements and weapons (actual size)
of the Ice Age (Stone Age) hunters.
Made of flint: A. Pick or knife B.
Scraper C. Serrated pick D. Bor-
ing tool. Made of bone or horn: E.
Needle with eye F. Harpoon G.
Spear point (engraved)*

rock face is crumbling, and in places the roof has caved in. But it was not these things that frightened the village folk the most. They believe to this very day that the cave is the haunt of ghosts. And they live in fear that anyone who enters the cave will be bewitched."

"Did Don Marcelino know this too?" asked Marcel.

"He certainly did," said the Abbé, "but that made him all the more eager to explore it, for he thought to himself: This belief is surely very old and points to the fact that the cave was a human dwelling in prehistoric times, and it may be worth while to look for traces of habitation there. And at any rate there is one good thing about this fear of 'ghosts': it has kept the village folk away from the cave, and I shall find everything there just as it was in the days before there were even plows. Full of confidence Don Marcelino began to explore the cave."

"And what about little Maria?" asked Simon. "I thought *she* was the discoverer."

"You shall hear about her presently," said the Abbé.

ABOVE: *Red sign (magic?), Altamira*
BELOW: *Section of ceiling of the Great Hall, Altamira*

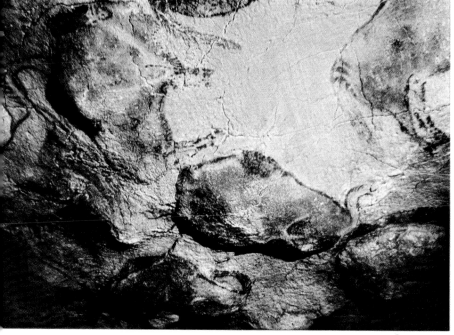

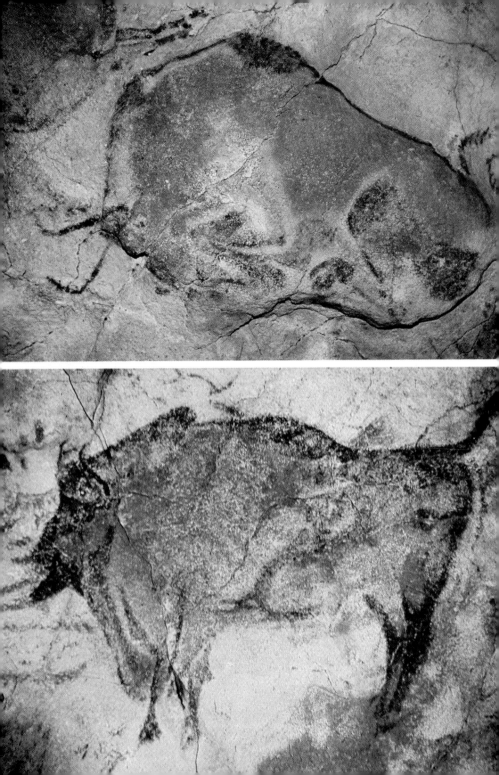

The Look in the Eye of the Bison

"Little Maria of Altamira was just nine years old when her father began digging in the cave that had been open to him for many years. He went into the cave often, and did not give up even though for a long time he brought home nothing from it but his tools.

"At last, one November day, he returned to his castle in the greatest excitement, without his tools, yet not with empty hands. He had found a bone point and a few flint scrapers like the ones he had seen in the glass cases in Paris. No living being could say to him: *I* saw those things before you did. . . . Don Marcelino had brought back proof that people of the Ice Age had lived on the land in which he now lived in his castle, and here had defended themselves against the great ice and the mighty beasts that threatened them. This proof could stand up to the most critical eyes: it could be *touched*.

"From that time Don Marcelino went digging day after day. He found the bones of a cave bear and all kinds of objects like those he had seen in the glass cases in Paris. And when he found a big bone with

ABOVE: *Bison lying down, Altamira*
BELOW: *Bison standing, Altamira*

drawings on it he went off to Madrid, the capital of Spain, and showed the drawings and some of the implements he had found to the most celebrated Spanish professor whose subject was archaeology or the exploration of the earth's past—his name was Vilanova. And this professor congratulated Don Marcelino on his finds and told him he should keep on digging, and if he found more things then he, the professor, would himself come to Altamira to examine the lot. And one day he came.

"But before this, something happened which no professor, not even the famous Professor Vilanova, could have foreseen.

"Don Marcelino had often taken Maria with him into the cave. The little girl enjoyed looking on while her father carefully scratched away one little bit of earth after another with a pick by the light of a few candles. Maria was pleased whenever something came to light which her father took in his hand and showed her. And sometimes, when he worked on for a long time turning up nothing but piles of earth, the little girl would run around in the cave. She did not fear the overhanging rocks, for a little imp of nine does not knock her head where a man has to stoop and therefore can hardly see what is above him.

"It was a November day, and only a faint ray of light entered the cave from the outside. Don Marcelino had brought more candles than usual with him, but he found nothing worth while. One lump of earth after another crumbled in his hands. Maria took a candle and started wandering about the cave. She

The great painted hunting frieze, Alpera.
In reality the upper part is left of the centerpiece,
the lower part, right

was bored and a bit uncomfortable too, for her fingers were getting cold. So she kept holding her hands in turn near the candle flame to warm them. Just for want of anything else to do, Maria shone the candle into the corners of the cave and lighted up the rock formations on the ceiling of a side chamber. The candlelight played on them and made them emerge from the shadows. Suddenly the little girl cried, 'Toros! Toros!' That's a Spanish word and means, 'Bulls! Bulls!' The child saw bulls standing or lying about, and they were not frightful to look at but magnificent, all in glowing red.

" 'Toros!' shouted the little girl once more, for she had never seen such beautiful bulls, at once so powerful and so tame.

"The father stopped to listen while a lump of clay broke up in his hand. Then he came out of the room near the entrance, and went into the side chamber.

" 'You see bulls, do you?' he asked. 'Where are the bulls?'

" 'There!' cried the little girl, lifting the candle up against the humps of rock on which the bulls were gleaming.

" 'Those are only shadows,' said the father. 'There's nothing to be frightened about.'

" 'I'm not afraid, Father,' said the child. 'But look, *next* to the shadow there's a bull, a red bull!'

" 'That's the light,' said her father. 'The candlelight is deceiving you.'

" 'No! No!' cried the little girl. 'There are a whole lot of bulls, and they're all red!'

"Don Marcelino wiped the earth from his hands, bent down, and crept in to where the girl was standing. 'We must go home,' he said. 'You've caught cold and you're feverish.' He laid his hand on the child's forehead.

"But then Don Marcelino shook his head, baffled. The child's forehead was cool. Maria wasn't running a high temperature. He knelt down and bent back. Then he examined the rock ceiling carefully, one hump after another. He saw nothing. Maria now gave him the candle, while she fetched the longest pick that Don Marcelino had brought. With it she pointed to a big reddish animal which appeared to be writhing as if it had been hurt.

" 'There! Look at its horns, and the hoofs on all the four feet, and look here at its big eye!' she cried.

"Then suddenly Don Marcelino saw the animal which Maria had taken for a bull. It was a bison in its death agony. It was looking down at them with its big eye, which had a black circle around it. And Don Marcelino saw the heavy shadow which the bison cast. The deep hollow beside it was filled with the shadow. The black made the red of the mighty bison's body glow forth more strongly. In the candlelight it seemed as if the beast were heaving itself up and breathing. But the eye was motionless. The look which came from it seemed to be its last. Don Marcelino breathed heavily. The candle flickered.

" 'Now the bull is moving!' cried Maria.

" 'No,' said the father. 'Don't be afraid. He can't

move. He's only made of paint and rock.' He clasped his little daughter to his breast while his glance wandered from one rock hump to another. On each of them he saw an animal."

The King Visits the Cave

"And now the famous Professor Vilanova came from Madrid. Don Marcelino had written to him after he had carefully examined the ceiling and walls of the cave by a good light in the days that followed, and found well over a hundred pictures.

"Again and again his hand had trembled with excitement, for instance when the lamp light fell on a wild boar which seemed to be heading for him, or when its rays touched the head of a grazing hind. The animals seemed so amazingly alive. True, they were only painted with color on cold stone—Don Marcelino knew that—yet they were not dead.

"It completely baffled him that he had been in the cave so often, yet had seen nothing. I hardly ever looked up, he thought. My eyes were continually on the ground. I was too eagerly burrowing in the earth. I was possessed with the desire to find something. The child was not looking for anything, and so she saw the animals at first glance.

"Professor Vilanova had looked at all Don Marcelino's finds in the castle. He had then examined all the places in the cave where they had been found. Now he was pushing his way from picture to picture.

"Don Marcelino noted with dismay how often the professor shook his head as if to say: That *cannot* be; such things simply *cannot* exist.

"But gradually he stopped shaking his head. The professor examined some of the pictures carefully, and he stopped a long time in front of the dying bison.

"Now the bison is looking at *him*, thought Don Marcelino.

" 'The colors are as fresh as if the pictures were painted only yesterday, don't you think?' he asked in a tone of suppressed excitement.

"The professor from Madrid made no reply. He had not even heard the question. He was lying on his back staring up at the ceiling which was not much more than three feet over him. He was as motionless as if he had been bewitched by the pictures. Don Marcelino noticed this, so he stopped asking questions until Vilanova turned to him.

" 'When was the cave discovered?' asked the professor.

" 'About ten years ago,' replied Don Marcelino.

" 'And you know all the people who have been in the cave since it was known to exist?'

" 'Yes, all of them,' said Don Marcelino. 'Apart from my gamekeeper and myself only a few village children have gone into the cave. And that was only for the first year; after that the parents forbade the children to enter it, because it's believed in the village that there are spirits in the cave. For years no one has been here except myself and Maria.'

"On hearing this, the professor was seized once more with the restless urge which, at the beginning, had driven him from picture to picture.

" 'There's been no artist here, then?' he asked, straightening up.

"Don Marcelino shook his head. Vilanova cautiously touched one of the pictures—he had already touched several others—and rubbed some of the color onto his hand. It was bright, shiny paint. Red, yellow, brown, and black dabs lay on the back of his hand.

" 'There are many pictures, and they're painted in different styles,' remarked Don Marcelino. 'And perhaps a more thorough search may reveal still more. But to paint even the pictures which we have found up to the present, a painter would need many years, don't you think?'

" 'Definitely,' said the professor. 'One human life would hardly be long enough.'

"He began once more to examine the pictures in the first chamber. Then the two searched in other parts of the cave. It was large and had many roomy side chambers. It reached about 390 yards into the bowels of the earth. In many parts of it they discovered more paintings, some of them greatly faded. Where the passage grew narrower Vilanova found little drawings which had been scratched with a spike on the soft walls. And in an alcove in which a kind of bench stood he found colored crayons. He took hold of a projecting

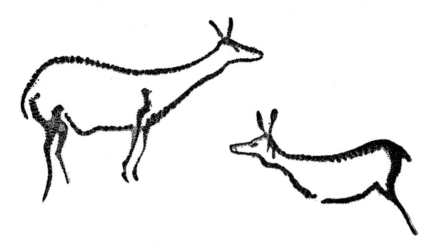

stone. It came away easily from the roof. Vilanova now noted with dismay that there were many cracks.

"On returning to the chamber where the many bison were, the professor examined the ceiling, hump by hump, for cracks. In many places the cracks went right through the pictures.

"Don Marcelino and Vilanova crouched down side by side and looked up. The ceiling was about thirty-three feet wide and double that in length, yet it was covered all over with life-sized pictures of animals, more than twenty-five of them. Sometimes one partly covered the other.

"There was a galloping horse, there were hinds, and above all there were bison. Many of these looked down at them boldly and fiercely. Their fearless eyes gripped the spectator. But the most impressive of all of them was the bison which Maria had seen first writhing in its death agony.

" 'A picture as fine as that one is seldom painted

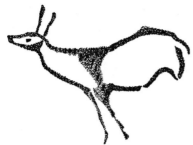

Three does, Covalanas (painted)

even once in a hundred years,' said the professor. 'No, indeed,' he continued, shaking his head with energy, as if he wished to shake off something that bothered him. 'No artist living today can have painted that picture.'

" 'So that's your firm belief?' asked Don Marcelino.

" 'Yes,' said the famous professor from Madrid.

" 'I have been keeping back something from you,' confessed Don Marcelino hesitantly, 'but now it can no longer mislead you. There *has* been a painter in Altamira within the past ten years.'

"The professor from Madrid looked at Don Marcelino in amazement.

" 'But,' continued Don Marcelino, 'he never entered the cave. I give you my word for that. He was an unfortunate fellow who had lost his speech through a shock when a child. I took him in to live at the castle, and he touched up some of the paintings in the castle which had become damaged in the course of years.'

" 'May I see one of his own paintings?' asked Vilanova.

" 'But surely you've noticed the picture which is in the room where I keep my collection of objects from the cave? That's his work.'

" 'That clinches the matter for me,' said the professor. 'The man who painted that picture has had nothing to do with these paintings.' He looked up once more at the bison. Then he grasped Don Marcelino's hand. 'There's not the slightest doubt about it,' he said. 'The pictures are at least ten thousand years older than any artist alive today.'

" 'It cannot be otherwise,' said Don Marcelino happily. 'But clearly no one would believe that from me, since I am not a professor.'

" 'But they will believe *me*,' said Professor Vilanova, as he walked back to the castle with Don Marcelino.

" 'It's a miracle that so many of the pictures are still in perfect condition after all this time,' said Don Marcelino.

" 'That's not the most wonderful thing about them,' remarked the professor. 'It is quite easy to explain that. They were down there in a constantly even temperature, in the darkness and silence, so hidden away that time no longer counted. They did not change, because no glance touched them, not even the glance of the sun. No hand ever touched them, because the cave guarded their secret well. It is not the great age of the pictures that is incomprehensible. The astounding thing about them is that they are *so good*. Some of these pictures are masterpieces, and the man who painted the dying bison will be accounted for all time one of the greatest painters in the world. One must remember that he painted his pictures at a time when a great part of the earth was buried under ice, and he had to contend with the bitter cold as well as with the lions and bears which were prowling around him. I believe that this was so, and I will back this belief with my name.'

"In Santander, the capital of the province, Professor Vilanova gave a lecture in which he revealed to a large audience that in the Ice Age human beings existed who were able not only to fight the woolly rhinoceros and the mammoth, the cave bear and the bison, and to cope with the Great Ice, but also to paint pictures, some of which were as good as any of the best pictures of later ages. 'And these pictures,' went on the famous professor from Madrid amid a silence which was almost as breathless as the silence in the cave of Altamira, 'these pictures were discovered by a child— by Maria, a nine-year-old girl. For many thousands of years they were enveloped in darkness. Now light has fallen upon them. They have been silent for a long time, but now they will speak, and the world will listen, because these pictures reveal what the human beings were like who lived in the age of the Great Ice.'

"In the days which followed people came in great numbers to Altamira to see the pictures. Newspapermen came, and these not only looked at the pictures, but questioned the professor from Madrid, and Don Marcelino, and the little girl. They wrote in many papers about the pictures which had been painted by

Wild horse in gallop, Altamira (painted)

men who had lived amid the Great Ice. A lot of fuss was made about the pictures. But down in the cave a deep hush always fell when the sight-seers caught the eye of the dying bison, or when the boar rushed at them, or one of the magnificent bison drew all eyes upon itself, leaving the beholders breathless with astonishment. All the papers wrote about the young discoverer, and many of them published her photograph."

"Will it be like that here in Montignac too?" Simon asked. "I mean, will there be a lot of fuss?"

He was not thinking at all of the fact that he might see his photograph in the newspapers. He was only afraid that some harm might come to the ponies and the deer if a lot of people visited them.

"Lots of people will come to visit *your* cave too,"

said the Abbé. "Newspaper articles and books will be written about these pictures. True, it is known today that great artists *did* live in the Ice Age. Scientists are continually searching for more cave pictures, but since the cave of Altamira no cave has been discovered which is as magnificent as this one. And your cave hides far more pictures than Altamira. But in one respect the Altamira girl's discovery towers above all other cave discoveries. That discovery was the first one that lifted the veil which had hidden the earliest human life from our sight. Since the day Maria pointed to the *'toros'* it has become possible to figure out from quite definite signs what the people of the Ice Age were like."

"And what were they like?" asked Marcel. "What is known about them?"

Three women, Valltorta Gorge (painted)

"You shall hear all that I know about them," said the Abbé. "But let us return now to the Altamira girl. In those days she was talked about throughout the whole world, just as if a miracle had happened through her. And then a great day came for her and for her father. Just think of it! One day the King of Spain came and stood before little Maria. Professor Vilanova had given him a report about the pictures.

"The avenue leading to the castle of Altamira had been decorated. Don Marcelino had had the mouth of the cave widened so that the King could enter easily. Servants stood ready with candles in their hands. It was like being in church, and the light of the many candles made the cave seem higher. But it was just the same as ever, and the King, too, had to bend down like everyone else when he entered the side chambers. When he wanted to look at the animals on the ceiling, he too had to make himself small. And he knelt down under the bison which gazed at him with the last look of its dying eye.

"The King remained a long time in the cave. He asked to be conducted to the very last niche. He did not mind having to crawl and crouch. The servants held the candles close up to the rock walls and to the ceiling, so that the King should not miss one single picture. And one of the servants secretly burned the name of the King—Alphonsus XII—into the rock at the entrance to the cave, so that all future visitors should see that a king had been among the earliest visitors of the cave.

"When the King had viewed all the pictures and

ABOVE: *Head of a bison cow, Altamira*
BELOW: *Standing bison, Altamira*

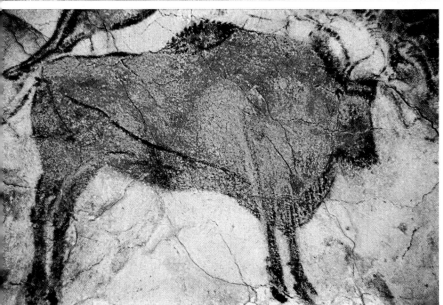

stepped out again into the open, a great crowd had gathered. They shouted enthusiastically as soon as they caught sight of him. But the King made a sign, and there was silence. He took little Maria by the hand, and in the presence of all the people he said, 'We have to thank you, little Maria, for this great discovery. Spain is proud of the girl of Altamira.'

"And all the people who were listening threw their hats in the air and shouted, 'Viva María! Viva el Rey! —Long live Maria! Long live the King!'

"It was a day of pride and glory. And the King said, 'Next year professors from the world over will be meeting in Lisbon to discuss the most important discoveries

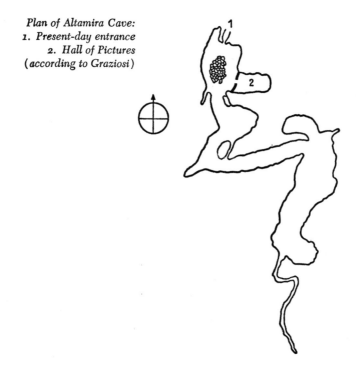

Plan of Altamira Cave:
1. Present-day entrance
2. Hall of Pictures
(according to Graziosi)

ABOVE: *Engraved bison, La Grèze*
BELOW: *Cattle on a stone block, Fournier du Diable*

of recent years. I shall invite them to come to Spain too. For Altamira seems to me to be the greatest of all discoveries of recent times.'

"With these words the King took his leave of them, and all the people could see that he was deeply moved."

"And what about the professors?" asked Jim, giving voice to what they all wanted to know. "The professors from all over the world—what did they say?"

"You'll be surprised," said the Abbé.

The Professors
from All Over the World

"Many professors met in Lisbon, in Portugal," continued the Abbé. "They came from all the countries in which there are professors, and they had all written books and were famous, at least in their own country. Many of them gave lectures in which they told the others about the researches they had been carrying out in the past few years. And after the lectures the professors talked their heads off among themselves.

"Vilanova gave a lecture about the cave paintings of Altamira. Everyone listened to him attentively, for Vilanova was a very famous scholar. He had gone to great trouble to copy a number of the pictures of Altamira. Many of these drawings were colored. After the lecture the professors examined them.

" 'How old might these pictures be?' asked a professor from Sweden.

" 'Ten to twenty thousand years old,' said Vilanova, 'perhaps even older. It is quite certain that the engravings in the narrow passage of the cave are older.'

" 'It's just as well that you say "perhaps," ' said a

professor from Italy, 'because it may also be that they are only ten or twenty years old.'

" 'Twenty thousand,' said Vilanova firmly.

" 'And how do you propose to prove to us this fabulously great age of the pictures?' asked a professor from America. 'Such pictures would be worth millions!'

" 'Their value could scarcely be calculated in figures,' said Vilanova. 'But their age, on the other hand, *can* be calculated with certainty. In the Altamira Cave, Don Marcelino de Sautuola has also found tools and objects which proved to be of the Ice Age—knives and scrapers such as have been found in some other countries already. He even found drawings on bone, similar to those we already know from other sites of discoveries.'

" '*Drawings*—now that's another matter,' said a professor from France, who himself had found similar drawings. 'Drawings can be accepted as proof, together with the tools which are known to have been used by men of the Ice Age. But colored pictures? Surely you do not think it possible that colored pictures can have been made with knives and flint tools?'

" 'No, I don't,' said Vilanova. 'The colors have been applied with color crayons, or with the fingers, or with brushes. No doubt an artist could determine the particular technique which has been used in applying the brush. But anyone can see with the naked eye that brushes have been used.'

" 'Have brushes of that period been found?'

" 'No, not brushes,' said Vilanova. 'They rotted long ago; but crayons, from the darkest brown to the brightest red. Don Marcelino found flat stones, too, on which paints had been ground and mixed. I have had the paints analyzed. They are made of ocher, and marl, and manganese, and of charcoal too. No doubt the moisture of the rock also helped to bind the colors. A set of color crayons was found lying on a stone bench in a hidden alcove of the cave of Altamira. The crayons lay there as if the artist had just put them down.'

" 'Twenty thousand years ago, eh?' added a professor from Portugal, amid laughter.

"Vilanova was silent. He looked into the faces of the professors who stood around him and his drawings. It was easy to see that he was in for a hard struggle. He was one against many. A superior force of doubters was attacking his belief in the genuineness of the cave paintings. And Vilanova knew that his reputation as a great scholar was at stake.

" 'Never before has anything of the kind been seen or heard of anywhere,' said the professors.

" 'What does that prove?' cried Vilanova. 'Everything must have a beginning. After all, paintings may yet be found in other caves too.'

" 'Where is our progress,' protested a professor from Switzerland, 'if man was already capable of producing perfect works of art twenty thousand years ago?'

" 'Did not the Egyptians, Chinese, Babylonians, and Chaldeans produce works of art thousands of years ago, which are no less valuable than the best of our age?' asked Vilanova. 'What right have we to think ourselves superior to people who lived long before us?

May it not be that the people of different epochs only speak different languages, but that in each age it is given to man to produce the highest in his own way? Why shouldn't we respect that nameless artist who painted the dying bison of Altamira so wonderfully that the sight of its death still grips all who see it?'

"A professor from Paris countered hotly: 'Because it is absolutely and utterly incredible that the people of the Ice Age—even assuming that there were artists of the highest rank among them—could have painted just as the best artists of Paris paint *today*. The works of art of the Egyptians and Babylonians have something strange, something primitive about them. But the cave pictures at Altamira are not strange, they are not "old." They speak a language which is suspiciously close to ours. No! No! Someone trying to palm off a hoax on the experts of the whole world has painted those pictures, or had them painted. . . .'

"Vilanova walked up to the professor from Paris. 'A Spanish nobleman has given me his word,' he said, 'that nobody but himself and his gamekeeper and a few village children entered the cave. Would you doubt the word of Don Marcelino?'

" 'A nobleman is not a man of learning,' said a professor. 'A nobleman can make a mistake when it is a question of science.'

" 'The King of Spain has invited you to inspect the pictures,' cried Vilanova, pale with anger.

" 'The King himself has been misled,' said a professor from Portugal, 'just as someone has tried to mislead us. Our unanimous rejection of the pictures will convince him, however, that the matter is a somewhat—er—disreputable one. The paint—you say so yourself—is as fresh as if it had been applied only recently?'

" 'There's nothing extraordinary in that,' cried Vilanova, 'since the cave was overgrown, sealed up in such a way that not a breath of air could touch the pictures. Besides, who could have painted hundreds of pictures secretly, and brought unnoticed into the cave the quantity of paint necessary for painting all those pictures?'

" 'The matter must be investigated!' cried some.

"Vilanova noticed a change in the faces of some of his learned colleagues. They had been scornfully incredulous; now they became suddenly thoughtful. For a moment even the most violent doubters seemed to be opening their minds to his point of view. But at this point a man stepped forward whom Vilanova recognized with alarm. He was a professor from Madrid. Vilanova remembered that he had once told this man about the artist whom Don Marcelino had taken to live in his castle. If it became known *now*, at this crucial moment, that a painter had been in Altamira during those years when the cave stood open . . .

" 'But you told me in Madrid,' declared this Spanish professor, 'that Don Marcelino had a painter staying in his castle for several years, just at that time.' With a voice growing louder and more excited, the professor from Madrid continued, 'A dumb painter, was he not? Perhaps Don Marcelino had his own reasons for

People and animals, Cogul (painted)

seeking out a painter who could not speak? Or perhaps it was Don Marcelino himself who made the painter dumb—with money?'

"A tumult broke out. Vilanova tried to speak. He shouted. But no one would listen to him and he was just left standing there. Vilanova stared at the backs turned on him as the professors left the hall in a body. He looked around. He was alone. And he was frightened."

The Abbé from Paris was silent. His eyes were on the ground.

"But he didn't give up, did he?" asked Marcel.

"There were too many against him," said the Abbé.

George flared up. "What?" he cried. "Did he leave Don Marcelino in the lurch?"

"It is no easy matter to stand alone in one's opinion," said the Abbé. "It is rare for anyone to hold out in such circumstances."

"But he had seen the pictures," said Marcel, "and anyone who had once seen the pictures . . ."

"Vilanova was a professor of high repute," said the Abbé. "He knew that if he held his ground he would be regarded as a fool by the most celebrated men of learning."

"But if he gave up Altamira he was a coward," said Jim.

"Did he really do that?" asked the boys all together.

"Yes, he did," said the Abbé. "But who knows? Perhaps I would have done the same."

The Montignac boys looked at the Abbé horrified.

"Never!" said Simon. He spoke for them all.

"That professor from Paris," said the Abbé seriously, "the one who got so worked up at the Congress in Lisbon, was my teacher, Émile Cartailhac. He was a man of the strictest honor and a scrupulous scholar. I owe him more than I can ever tell. Almost everything that I know about cave paintings I learned from him. But in those days he still did not believe in Altamira, and he remained unbelieving for fully twenty-three years, although a distinguished archaeologist named Lartet had already, back in 1864, unearthed a piece of a mammoth's tooth with the figure of a mammoth engraved on it. Cartailhac remained skeptical until cave pictures were found painted on rock which itself produced the proof of the age of the pictures—by a layer of deposit (stalactite) which could only have accumulated in thousands of years, as was the case with the pictures discovered by Gaston. Indeed, even then this man remained skeptical. It was only when five picture caves had been discovered and it was possible to make comparisons, that Cartailhac withdrew his rejection of Altamira."

The boys were silent. The Abbé looked at them, one after another.

"But the professors were blind. They didn't want to see," said Marcel.

"Yes, that seems to be the fate of great discoveries," replied the Abbé. "Only very few people have courage enough to believe in them from the beginning."

"You would never have let Don Marcelino down like that," declared Marcel solemnly. But just at that moment his light became so dim that Jim had to switch on his or they would have been left sitting in the dark.

"And what happened in Altamira after that?" asked Jim, holding his torch focused on the roof. "I suppose the day for the professors' visit to the cave was arranged a long way ahead?"

"Yes, months ahead," said the Abbé. "No one thought they could possibly refuse. The front pages of all the newspapers in Spain and Portugal, and also of many newspapers in the other countries which had sent professors to Lisbon, had articles with big headlines:

Headings like this appeared in all the papers. Don
Marcelino had prepared everything as carefully as
possible. He was eager to do honor to these famous
men, who would find in him a host of whom the King
of Spain might be proud.

"But not one came.

"A telegram arrived from Vilanova. It was followed
by a lengthy letter in which he explained that he had
been unable to maintain his opinion any longer against
the weight of conflicting proofs. . . ."

"The traitor!" cried Marcel.

"And what did Don Marcelino do?" asked Jim.

"For several days nobody saw him outside the
castle," said the Abbé. "In his room the same deep
silence reigned that had reigned in the cave while it
was sealed up. When he emerged for the first time
after a week and went up to the hill of Altamira once
more, his hair was white. There was not a soul in the
cave. His first glance fell on the big letters which had
been burned with a candle: Alphonsus XII.

"I won't turn to him, thought Don Marcelino. I will
take it upon myself, myself alone, to fight for the truth.

"The articles about Altamira which appeared in the
newspapers in the following days no longer mentioned
the paintings but only the man who had drawn attention to them.

These were the types of headlines which *now* appeared in the papers. Nothing but mockery and suspicion on all sides. And some of the newspaper headings read:

DON MARCELINO'S MYSTERIOUS GUEST
THE PAINTER WITH THE SEALED MOUTH
WHO WAS THE PAINTER OF ALTAMIRA?

"Many of the newspapers started to ask about the artist who, according to Don Marcelino, had never entered the cave and had lost his speech in childhood."

"But surely Don Marcelino was telling the truth?" asked Jim.

"The absolute truth," the Abbé assured him. "The artist was already dumb when he became a guest at Altamira. During the years that he spent painting at the castle he never once entered the cave."

"And why did he not come forward to testify to the truth?" asked Marcel.

"He did come forward," said the Abbé. "As soon as he read in the papers that he and Don Marcelino were accused of fraud, he came."

"But before that," asked George, "at the time when so many people were coming to Altamira—did he never enter the cave in those days?"

"No," said the Abbé.

"But why didn't he?" asked Simon.

"I shall tell you that presently," replied the Abbé.

The Artist with the Sealed Mouth

The Abbé turned to Marcel. "Weren't you the first to enter the cave?" he asked.

"Yes," said Marcel. "But Simon wanted very much to get there before me."

"That doesn't matter now," continued the Abbé. "I only want to know how you felt when you crept through the narrow entrance."

"I was thinking of Robot," said Marcel readily, "and that helped me."

"Would you have gone on crawling in even if Robot hadn't been in the cave?" the Abbé questioned him.

"I probably would have. I'm crazy about caves and things like that."

"And you think that anyone would have crept through that narrow hole?"

"How do I know?" said Marcel hesitantly. "Perhaps not everyone. It wasn't very comfortable. Perhaps some people would have been afraid. But if you're not a sissy . . . Every real boy likes adventure and belongs to some gang." Marcel stopped short, seeing that the Abbé was beginning to smile.

And then the Abbé said, "If the only real boys are the ones who belong to some gang and like exploring caves, then Henry—for that was the name of the artist —never was a real boy in his life. Henry liked being alone. He would rather be alone with his own thoughts than be with other boys. The others called him a dreamer, but they all liked him although he kept to himself. He never did anything that a boy would consider dishonorable. At school he was always ready to help a boy who had got into trouble. He could think more quickly than most and draw better than any of them. He also made the best bows and arrows, and he had a marvelous knack for finding the most suitable wood. He also had an uncanny eye for unusual stones and plants; they seemed to attract him. So the others often asked him to join them in their games and pranks. Now and then he went along and if he did, he put his whole heart in it, so that he did better than the rest of them. When they played 'fox and hounds' he used to volunteer eagerly to be the 'fox' and let the 'hounds' hunt him. And it often took an hour or more to catch him. He never shirked the fight either, when they ran him to earth. He would fight so fiercely, and would jump on the 'hounds' so wildly that he knocked them down and many a time they had to beat a retreat. At such times the shy, quiet boy who had lost his mother at birth turned into a real tough guy. Seeing him fight when cornered, you would have thought he would make a first-rate leader for the gang.

"But Henry wasn't really tough at heart; he was no leader by nature. He fought, not for the love of fighting, but only for fear of being laughed at by the others. He wasn't thrilled by adventures. He was always glad when they were over. But he wasn't going to be a sissy and so he forced himself never to let others notice that he was always frightened in danger, and that he hated to get into real trouble. For that very reason he often risked more than the others.

"One day he was again the 'fox' running before the hounds. He was a quick runner. With his hands cupped over his mouth he shouted up at the walls of rock, so that his voice would echo from the opposite direction. But although he threw the 'hounds' off the scent again and again, he was at last surrounded. The leading 'hound' had placed a few 'sentry hounds' at special points, and Henry had to take care, while he ran zigzag, not to get too near any of them. He was already

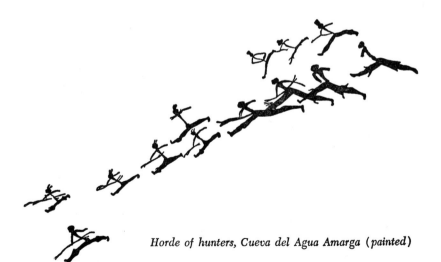

Horde of hunters, Cueva del Agua Amarga (*painted*)

rather out of breath when he caught sight of a 'sentry hound' only about thirty yards away. He saw a red face out of which came a cry when Henry stopped short. He was spotted. At the yelp of the 'sentry hound' the pack would sight him.

"Henry was done in. He felt weak. For the first time he would be unable to put up a good fight and would be just shamefully run down. He saw a few 'hounds' away to the left. They were so near that he could recognize their faces. A panicky fear seized him. He wanted to avoid this fight for which he no longer had strength. He looked around for a hiding place, then began to run wildly. His flight was no longer a game now; it was serious. He tasted blood in his mouth. As he raced along he caught sight of an opening in the ground. It was a fox hole or a badger's burrow. Henry threw himself face downward and forced his way into the hole. Although it was narrow, he pushed himself in farther and farther. My feet must still be outside, he thought, and he tried to jerk himself deeper into the burrow. Then suddenly he felt a terrible weight on his back. He could no longer breathe or open his mouth. He tried to cry out, but he couldn't. The burrow had caved in. Henry was buried under it.

"It lasted only a few seconds, for in the same moment the 'hounds' had turned back into boys, into buddies who took hold of him. They got him out straight away, two boys pulling at each leg. And Henry could hear them laughing although he had sand in his ears. They laughed because his legs looked so funny sticking out of the ground. And now they went

ABOVE: *Small head of a horse, Las Chimeneas*
BELOW: *Stag, Las Chimeneas*

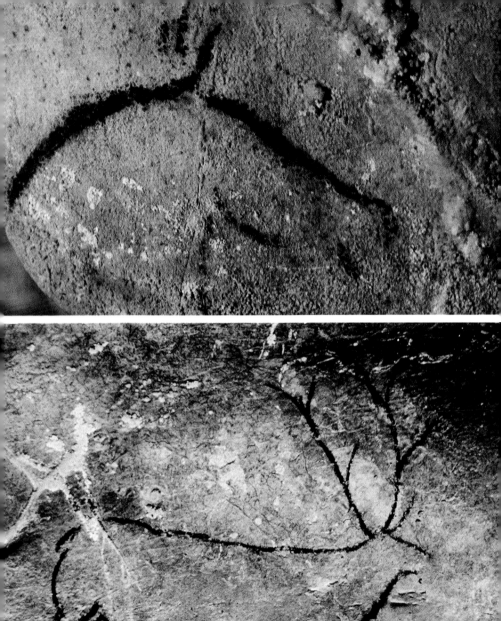

Ibex, Ebbou (engraved)

on laughing because he looked so disheveled, and because everything seemed to have ended so well.

" 'Tell us, fox, what was it like in the fox hole?' one
of them asked him.

"Henry opened his mouth, but no word came out

Ibexes, partially overlaid with stalactite, Cougnac.

of it. Nothing came out but sand, which Henry spat out. He wiped the sand from his eyebrows and eyelashes too. Happily none had got into his eyes, as they had closed tight when the hole fell in. And now these eyes stared at the other boys, and at the trees around. They were wide, wide open. Henry looked very queer. It was all a little uncanny. The boys' laughter died away.

" 'But it's all over now,' said the leader of the gang. He felt like taking Henry by the shoulders and shaking him, but somehow he did not dare. 'You were never such a fine fox as this time,' he said. 'You'd got us all dead beat, and you led us by the nose.'

"Henry opened his mouth again. They could see clearly that he was saying something. But none of them could understand him. Not a sound came out.

" 'Why don't you say something?' asked the youngest of the boys. 'The game is over now, isn't it?' "

"Yes, why didn't he say anything?" Simon asked the Abbé.

"Because he couldn't," said the Abbé. "He could not utter a word. The fright he had got had robbed him of the power of speech."

"Henry went to a school for the deaf and dumb. There too he was at the head of the class. He was a good artist, and he also learned to play the violin. But he did not learn to speak again. Now you know why the dumb artist avoided the cave of Altamira. Because the earth had pinned him down in such a terrifying way the first time he had ventured into it, he did not trust it any more."

"But when the pictures were discovered, didn't that attract him?" asked Marcel. "I mean, on account of the pictures?"

"Yes, it did attract him," said the Abbé. "He would have given a great deal to see the pictures. But he had heard that many people had cast doubts on these pictures, and he did not wish to remind people of himself, as this could only nourish their stupid suspicions. Or perhaps he only said this to himself to make it easier for him to keep away from the pictures. For these mysterious pictures attracted him more powerfully than any pictures had ever done before."

"I can understand all that," said Marcel. "But what did he do when the newspapers began asking about him, and when Don Marcelino was accused of being a swindler?"

"He wrote to Don Marcelino at once," said the Abbé. "In that letter he described the 'fox hunt' I've just told you about, and he assured Don Marcelino that since then he had never entered a cave. But now he asked to be allowed to look at the pictures in the cave. Perhaps he, the artist whom people suspected, could find something in the pictures through which it could be proved that they were as old as Don Marcelino assumed and as he, Henry, also believed that they were.

"Don Marcelino asked the mute artist to come as quickly as possible. He had decided to take up the fight for the cave. The haste with which the newspapermen seized upon anything which could prove sensational, the lack of scruple with which they wrote one thing today and something else tomorrow, had awakened the anger and defiance of the Spanish nobleman. He wanted to fight back. Perhaps the artist would discover something that would silence the slanderous tongues.

"As soon as he got Don Marcelino's letter the artist set out for Altamira. Don Marcelino took Maria with him when he went with Henry to the cave. He had given much thought to what was best for the artist. His idea was to let the child go in first. If Henry saw her get through, he might not find it so hard. On the way Don Marcelino talked about the great number of people who had been in the cave, and what a lot of room there was inside. 'In many places,' he went on casually, 'it's so high that one can stand up and walk around. And the most important pictures are not in the narrow passage but in the large chamber.'

"When the entrance, which had been widened, came into view, Don Marcelino said, 'It's almost like the doorway of a church, isn't it?' But actually he need not have worried in the least.

"Henry was not thinking at all of that fox hole of long ago, as he walked toward the cave that day. He had only one thought: What will the pictures be like? The nearer he got to the entrance, the more he felt drawn toward it. And suddenly he felt as if he were a boy of your age again, with a longing to play the wild, exciting game once more."

"The fox-and-hounds game?" asked Simon.

"Yes, exactly," said the Abbé. "The game in which he was one against the gang and knocked down his pursuers, or at least some of them."

"But he was a man then, and not a boy!" said George, amazed.

"He was an artist," said the Abbé; and for a few moments he was silent, lost in thought. Then, with glowing eyes, he continued: "I will try to tell you what an artist is. If I don't, you won't be able to understand what happened that day in the cave. If I succeed in making clear to you how a picture comes into being, then the pictures there over your head, which you discovered, will have a lot more meaning for you than they had before." The Abbé raised his hand and pointed to the line of little trotting horses.

"Just paint," said the Abbé, "nothing more."

"Ponies," said Simon very decidedly.

"Paint," repeated the Abbé. "You can see for yourselves, can't you, that there's nothing but paint there. There was paint on Marcel's fingertips."

"We know now that it's paint," said Marcel, "but at first we thought: There are horses and stags and ponies. We thought there were live animals in front of us."

"Simon shouted out quite loud: 'There's a horse!'" said Jim. "And we were all frightened, and then George and I saw the cows and the stags. And when Marcel saw the horse he thought at first: There's a horse. And he couldn't understand at all that there was paint on his finger when he touched the horse ever so carefully."

"Yes," added George, "all four of us thought at first: Those are animals. Perhaps they're ghost animals, but they're certainly animals."

Herd of wild horses, Limeuil (engraved on a sheet of stone)

"You see, the ponies are trotting," said Marcel. "They're full of life; and the two dark-red bisons are just this minute starting to run away. The stags are really swimming, the painter has got them so wonderfully."

"He's 'got' them; that's just the word!" exclaimed the Abbé. And then, speaking so softly that the boys had to listen with all their ears, he went on: "A hunter could not have 'got' them better. Now the artist's eye has to hit the deer just like a shot. The artist's eye dare not be unsure; his hand dare not tremble. Otherwise the artist does not 'get' what he is aiming at."

"But when a hunter aims well at an animal he kills it," retorted Jim quickly.

"An artist . . ." said Marcel; and he groped for words to express himself: "An artist is a hunter too.

But *he* doesn't kill; instead, he brings to life what his eye hits."

"Exactly!" cried the Abbé, overjoyed that the boys had grasped his meaning so perfectly. "The animal which an artist has really 'got' breathes, gives out warmth, looks at you. I've told you about the look on the face of the bison which held the eyes of little Maria of Altamira, and of Don Marcelino, and of the professor from Madrid, and of the King of Spain. One can forget a look: the king did so. One can be afraid of a look: that's why the professor from Madrid never came back. But the bison's gaze gave new courage to Don Marcelino every time he met it.

"And now the speechless artist had come, and was about to meet the bison's gaze. An artist is a hunter, as Marcel says, a hunter who brings something to life when he aims at it and hits the mark exactly.

"When an artist sets about making a picture, let's say, for instance, a picture of a lion, he records this lion with his eye again and again until he knows it by heart; until he begins to dream about it. He is seized by the animal which he wants to paint. It holds him, it haunts him, it never lets him go again, but dogs his steps. Finally, it affects him as the hounds affect the fox in that wild game which the other boys played with Henry before he lost his speech. However exhausted he is by being pursued, the artist must one day stand and face this lion that is following him day and night. He dare not relax, he dare not let himself be knocked down. He has to overcome his weakness and tackle it with all his might. And then all of a sudden, the hunted becomes the hunter once more. He aims with his eyes. And with this artist's glance a part of himself enters into the animal which he paints. And that is the power which makes the painted animal breathe. That is the life which can never again be taken out of the picture."

Little Simon nodded eagerly, and the Abbé continued: "I think that now, and only now, you will be able to understand the thing that happened to the dumb artist in the cave of Altamira.

"Henry became extremely excited as he got near the pictures. He did not even see the name of the king. I am certain, too, that he did not notice that he had to bend down at the spot where the roof began to get low. Don Marcelino had a good lamp with him, and Maria was carrying a candle as she had done when she discovered the pictures.

The artist knelt down on his right knee, bent aside, and propped himself on one elbow, in order to see better. He saw the pictures straight away. First he noticed some of the bison which were standing. Then he saw the prostrated beast. And he gazed into the black, wide-open eye. The dumb artist ran his eyes over the horns, the high-arched withers, the back, the chest, and the hoofs placed close to each other.

" 'How wonderfully the animal lies there!' he exclaimed. 'How perfectly it is adapted to the contour of the rock!' he shouted in a loud voice. One could sense his tense excitement from the words."

"But he couldn't talk at all!" said Simon.

"He was able to talk once more," said the Abbé, "but he himself didn't notice it. The girl was so amazed that she let the candle drop. At this the artist himself became aware of what had happened to him.

" 'Did I speak?' he asked, but stopped immediately when he realized that he had answered his own question. Don Marcelino noticed that he was beginning to tremble.

" 'What did you say about the contour of the rock?' asked Don Marcelino, just as if nothing had happened.

"Henry kept looking at the bison until he had recovered command of himself. Then he went on talking as if he had never been dumb, and pointed out to Don Marcelino how wonderfully the shape of the rock had been used to lend depth to the picture, and how the paint had been applied. 'Here,' he said pointing to the flank and to the hind legs, 'in these parts the paint must have been applied with a very fine brush, I should think probably with a feather. And here it's been smeared on with the fingers, and this line here has been drawn with a crayon.' "

"Did he say nothing about the bison's eye?" asked Marcel. "Surely that was the most important thing?"

"No," said the Abbé. "He said nothing at all about all the things that I've told you. As an artist, he was above all interested in *how* the other man had done it. He tried to get behind the other man's tricks, so to speak, as a hunter would. Then he drew Don Marcelino's attention to pictures drawn only in outline.

" 'Those must be much earlier than the colored ones,'

99

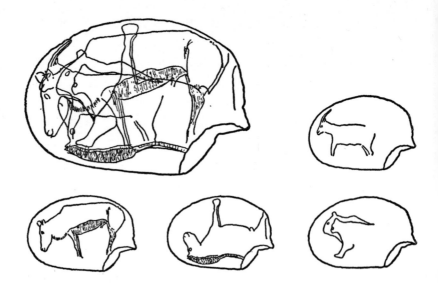

"Sheet of sketches" on both sides of a piece of flint (in each case different animals engraved one over another), La Colombière. The flint is 7¼ inches in diameter.

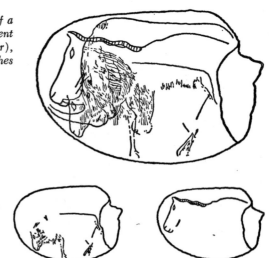

he said, 'because that is the way an artist begins.' He was able to account for many things as if he had been looking on when they were done.

" 'And how old are the pictures?' Don Marcelino asked him.

" 'That I don't know,' said Henry. 'They may be very old, but one cannot tell that just by the look of them.' "

The boys looked at the Abbé deeply disappointed.

"But wasn't the age of the pictures more important for Don Marcelino than anything else?" asked Marcel. "What he wanted most was for the artist to find some clue . . . on account of the newspapermen and the professors. Isn't that so?"

"In that hour," said the Abbé, "Don Marcelino no longer thought of the fuss the newspapers had made, or of how deeply the professors had offended him. All the stupid and malicious things that had been said about Altamira and had so excited the whole world lost their importance in the presence of the pictures. Through these pictures one artist had spoken to another across countless ages, and the other artist had answered him although he had been dumb. And just as the artist's affliction had left him, so too Don Marcelino suddenly felt himself free from all anxiety about what people call 'honor,' or 'reputation,' or 'good name.' Down there in the cave both men, the discoverer and the artist, were safe from the world. A great shell, as it were, protected them both from every hostile influence. They were there only for the pictures, and the pictures were there only for them.

"Henry made one discovery after another. He pointed out places where the paint was applied so that the rock shone through. It could not have been applied either with the hand or with a brush. 'The paint must have been blown on here,' he remarked to Don Marcelino. 'The painter must have blown it onto the rock, perhaps from his open hand, or perhaps through a tube.'

" 'That is quite possible,' said Don Marcelino, 'I have found hollow bones with traces of paint on them. The paint was mostly inside, and I couldn't explain it to myself at all.'

" 'Look over here,' said the artist. 'This horse has been chiseled into the rock, perhaps with a sharp knife or a scraper. The lines have been drawn with such a sure hand that not one stroke has had to be improved. The man who did that must have drawn many hundreds of horses before he engraved this horse in the rock.'

" 'I have found drawings of horses on the shoulder blades of stags and on flat stones,' said Don Marcelino.

" 'That artist must definitely have had a teacher,' said Henry, 'and it is equally certain that his teacher must have been taught in a school in his time. An artist who has to begin from scratch and has no pattern to follow will never develop fast enough to draw bison like the ones on the roof with the many humps.'

"Don Marcelino now conducted Henry to a part of the cave where a great many lines were scratched side by side on the rock face. 'What did the artist mean by these?' he asked, looking at Henry inquiringly.

" 'No artist drew those lines,' said Henry without hesitation. 'That was an animal. Those lines were made by an animal's claw. A bear sharpened his claws here. I've seen claw marks like those in the Zoo.'

" 'Perhaps when the Ice Age man saw those claw marks,' said Don Marcelino, 'it occurred to him that he also could draw lines on rock. At first he was clumsy, but gradually he became more skillful. Then, one fine day, the first animal head appeared among the tangle of scratches. The cave bear was possibly the first drawing master of the cave man.'

" 'If that was the case,' said Henry, 'the pupil far surpassed his teacher.'

" 'That is not surprising,' said Don Marcelino. 'In everything else too he excelled the beasts which he encountered. And those were mighty beasts with which he had to contend day after day. Yet he held the field against them all.'

" 'And how did he do that?' asked the artist. 'He had against him the horns of the bison, the frightful weapons of the woolly rhinoceros, and the claws of the cave lions.'

" 'But man was able to do what no lion could achieve,' said Don Marcelino. 'He made himself weapons.'

"And Don Marcelino, who had found enough weapons in the cave of Altamira to give him a good idea of the matter, went on to describe how the men of the Ice Age grew more and more skillful in dealing with the dangers which surrounded them."

"And won't you tell us something about that, too?"

pleaded Marcel. "Something about the weapons of the hunters who conquered those gigantic animals?"

"Why, yes, certainly," said the Abbé. "We know more about them today than was known in Don Marcelino's time, for several decades have passed since then, and the scholars have not wasted time."

"How was it at the very beginning?" asked Simon. "What was the very first weapon of man?"

"Macaroni" drawings made with the fingers on the soft subterranean ground: mammoths and a snake, Baume-Latrone

An Arrow Speeds over the Valley

"In the beginning was the hand," began the Abbé. "But the day was to come when that hand would seize a stone, perhaps in a moment of great danger. The man was chasing a deer, let us say, when suddenly he saw a bear standing before him. The man stopped short, startled; the bear began to growl. The bear was starving. Once before it had killed a man; hence it was a bear which had lost its fear of man—of paws that had no claws. The bear rose threateningly on its hind legs and came nearer. The man saw there was no avoiding the fight, in which only one would survive. The man decided to pounce at the bear's throat and choke it.

"He crouched, the better to leap. He ducked so low that his fingers touched the ground. And with the fingers of his right hand he felt a stone. The man grabbed the stone; he grasped it firmly in his fist, and now the man's fist was twice as big as before. The stone had a sharp edge which stuck out between his nails and the ball of his thumb. The man did not see this, for he had eyes only for the bear, and his eyes

Cave bear walking, Les Combarelles (engraved)

never left the bear for one second. The man fixed the bear with his eyes, which now began to glitter, for now the man had a paw which was heavier than the bear's paw. Now he no longer need choke the bear; he could strike it instead.

"The man rose quickly from the ground. As he sprang up he delivered his blow, hitting the mark exactly—right over the bear's eyes. The bear tumbled over, and when the man came down on him and choked him, he put up no defense. That had never happened to the man before. The bear lay motionless. The man began to touch the bear cautiously. He lifted its paw; it fell back. The head dropped when the man

ABOVE: *Mammoth and aurochs, Pech-Merle (Cabrerets)*
BELOW: *Mammoth, Pech-Merle (Cabrerets)*

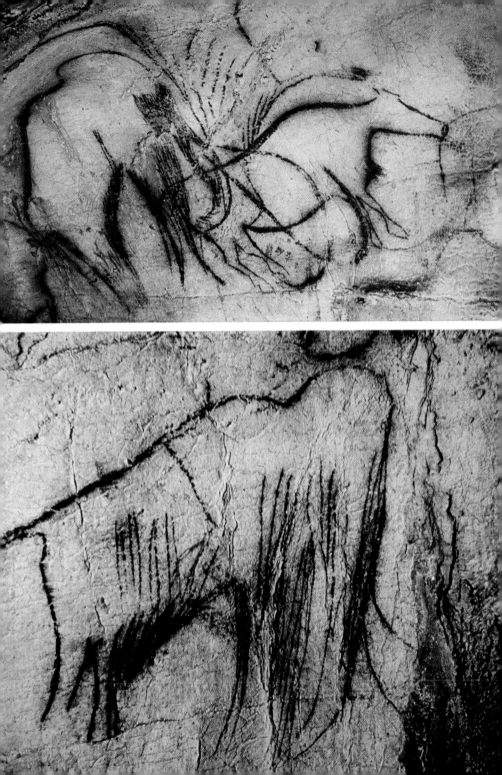

turned it. And then the man perceived that the stone which he had held in his fist was stuck between the bear's eyes. The stone had penetrated the skull over the eyes. The man drew it out with difficulty.

"You have saved me, stone, thought the man. If you had not come to my aid, it would be *I* and not the bear who would be lying here now, for it was the strongest animal I had ever met.

"The man examined the stone attentively. He drew his fingertips over its sharp edge. My fist has not got that edge, thought the man. I cannot smash in a bear's skull with my bare hand. This heavy sharp stone is a good thing.

"The man was very pleased with himself for having found the stone.

"The stone put itself into my hand, he thought. It wanted to come to me, and now we two belong together. For what good is the stone without my hand? Alone, it can do nothing but lie there. It is only in my hand that it is powerful. And only if I aim exactly and strike well can the stone kill a bear.

"The man shut his eyes and once more he saw himself leaping up and killing the bear with the stone.

"It is a good thing that my arm is so long and can reach out so far to deliver a blow, he thought. If my arm were shorter, its force would not be so great. Bears have hard skulls; a man cannot have enough force in dealing with them. If only my arm were longer, I could perhaps smash in a bison's skull. A longer arm would be a fine thing, but I can't make my arm grow any longer, reflected the man. He still had

Bisons from the Black Hall, Niaux

his eyes shut, and he began to dream that he had a longer arm. . . . His right arm was longer than his left, and with this much longer arm he saw himself swinging a sharp stone against the head of the bison. He saw in imagination an arm which he had not got at all. . . .

"In the beginning was the vision—the vision which man saw in his mind. Man began to look around for the longer arm of which he had dreamed. One day the man found a branch which had broken off a tree. The branch had a split like a gaping mouth with two open jaws. It made the branch look as if it were hungry. The man studied it, and then he looked at his stone. And then he stuffed the stone into the gaping mouth of the branch. And to make sure that the branch

Bison stricken by arrows, Niaux.
The bison is painted black, the arrows tipped with red

Woolly rhinoceros, Font-de-Gaume (painted)

would never again look as if it were hungry, the man lashed the stone in between the jaws of the branch's mouth in such a way that the sharp edge stuck out, as it had stuck out between his fingernails and the ball of his thumb. And then, wild with joy, the man swung this much longer arm, which was now really his own. He went for the head of a bison that a cave lion or a bear had killed, and with this long arm of his he smashed the bison's head. The sharp fist penetrated, the edge bit into the skull. The man had an ax.

"He kept on looking for better stones, and from these stones he fashioned sharper and sharper edges. but even with the sharpest ax he had to go so near the bear or the bison or the boar that they could wound him with their horns, claws, or hoofs. And when he threw the ax at the wild beast it did not have the same force as when he swung it. And once the ax had left his hand he was without a weapon.

"Then he thought to himself: A second, longer arm would be a good thing, perhaps one even longer than an ax; an arm with which to strike, or aim more accurately when he threw. So the man got long, straight branches, and practiced throwing them. He peeled the bark from a young ash sapling, and pointed the end of it; but the wooden point quickly became blunted. The horn of a bison would not become blunted, thought the man to himself; neither would the antlers of a stag. So he took the spike of an antler and fastened it firmly to his shaft. He became more and more expert in fashioning antlers or long bones into points for his shafts. Finally he had a good spear, with a barbed hook. It was in fact a kind of harpoon. When the man thrust

Wounded stag engraved with fine lines, La Peña de Candamo

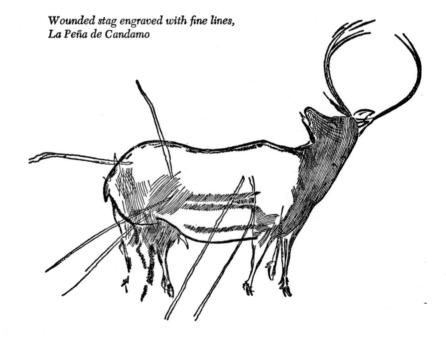

Bison, horse's head, and stakes (trap?), Pindal (painted and engraved)

it into a bison's body the animal could not shake it off. It made a frightful wound from which the bison bled to death.

"But the bison was swifter than the man. The stag too was swifter than he. He could only kill the doe with a harpoon at a short range. The man could stalk quite well, but not as well as a wolf could.

"If only I had a harpoon which would fly farther, thought the man.

"Then one day, when he was hunting a stag, he got

caught in the strong branch of a tree. The branch recoiled and flung the man to the ground.

"A harpoon propelled by a branch, that would be a good idea, thought the man as he picked himself up. With both hands he flexed a branch, and then let go with one hand so that it sprang back. He took a length of hide and bent the branch harder. Then, with this bent bow, he shot a stone from the bowstring. The smaller the stone was, the farther it sped. It must be a *small* harpoon, thought the man. He went on trying one thing after another. He made a string from the guts of animals, and with it he spanned the branch. He made the harpoon shorter and shorter, until finally

Three archers, freely grouped,
Valltorta Gorge (painted)

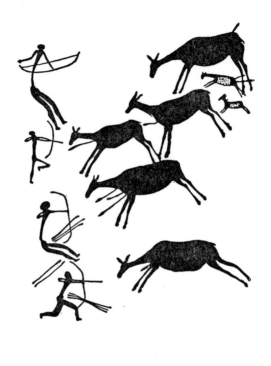

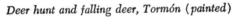

Deer hunt and falling deer, Tormón (painted)

it was no longer than his arm and as slender as his little finger. Then, one day, the first arrow sped forth from the bowstring.

"In the beginning was the thought.

"The arrow proved swifter than the deer, swifter than the wild horse. It was almost as swift as man's desire. But there were animals which neither arrow, nor harpoon, nor ax could hurt. To face the mammoth or the woolly rhinoceros these weapons were just absurd. The woolly rhinoceros did not even give a start

Wounded bison, Niaux. The round holes which were made by drips from the roof were utilized by the artist to represent the eye and also wounds. A ridge in the rock was made to serve as backbone. The rest is engraved

when a harpoon struck its armor; it just continued to hurtle down on the man like a great rock. And the mammoth bore down on him like a mountain, and ground him and his weapons to nothing.

"One night the man was sitting at an open fire at the mouth of his cave. Suddenly he saw a woolly rhinoceros emerge into view; he watched as it stopped, startled, and then took flight.

"Never before did a rhinoceros flee from me, thought the man. It must be the fire which frightened it. In future I will make a fire to keep off the beasts that are stronger than I am. So, the following nights, he took dry branches which burned well, and went out with these blazing branches to the place where he knew the rhinoceros to be. It made off as soon as it saw the fire.

Horse's head (life size)
Bédeilhac (engraved)

"Some hunters joined together. They formed a chain of men, each carrying a torch. They drove the woolly rhinoceros before them toward a precipice. The rhinoceros fled before them, and as soon as it got near the abyss the hunters started running more wildly. They brandished their torches, whirling them to form glowing circles in the darkness. Sparks flew in all directions. The rhinoceros raced off in a panic. It noticed too late that the ground was coming to an end under its feet, and that a void was opening. It rushed headlong to its death. Thus the woolly rhinoceros, the strongest animal next to the mammoth, was vanquished.

"In the beginning was the fire.

"Where there was no precipice at hand men made

a trap. They dug deep pits and covered them with branches and moss. They gathered in a wide circle around the place where they knew the mammoth was. Then, with terrifying shouts, they closed in with their torches. The mammoth often broke through a gap between two hunters, but sometimes their method was successful. Bison, wild horses, and wild cattle were also lured into traps, or into camouflaged corrals which collapsed as soon as an animal hit them. Of all ways of killing wild animals this was the least dangerous.

"Wild horses out grazing were approached by other wild horses. Suddenly these others threw off everything horselike and became those frightful creatures which gallop around on two feet, popping up wherever the wild horses would turn, flinging spears and swinging axes. . . . Hunters became more and more expert at moving about like animals, and they kept on thinking up new tricks. Above all, they learned to act in groups and to encircle their prey. For one hunter alone a fight with a bison or a bear or a rhinoceros was a life-or-death struggle. But the horde was stronger than even the mammoth. The horde had learned to plan in advance. It had many thoughts that became one plan and one will.

"In the beginning was the horde.

"The horde was stronger than the herd. With the horde began the time of man's domination over the beasts. One can read all that," concluded the Abbé, "from weapons which have been found in cave dwellings."

Hunter and two stags,
Valltorta Gorge (painted)

"And why," asked Simon, "do you always say: 'In the beginning was . . . ?'"

"Yes," said Marcel, "what was really in the beginning—the hand or the vision, the thought, the fire, or the horde?"

"They all were," said the Abbé, "each in its own time. For man was always moving forward. And that was man's good fortune. The bison and the woolly rhinoceros remained as they were with their horns; the boar remained with his tusks. They learned nothing new, and they did not change. But man, on the contrary, was not content with what he had once thought out or had learned from his forefathers. When he found that an ax would help him to deal with bears and lions but was useless against wild horses in full gallop, he did not rest until he had found something which would help him to cope with wild horses too. I said at first: In the beginning was the hand . . . That is true for a certain time. But even before this beginning, even before the first human hand grasped a stone, there existed something, the only thing which first made man into a being who was chosen to go farther than all other living beings: in the beginning was the spirit —the intellect—the spirit that was breathed into man; that raised him up and bade him walk upright, with his head raised toward the sun. His intellect made man so alert that, though sometimes defeated, he could no longer be displaced from his position of mastery. Finally there was not a wild beast left that could endanger the hunting horde or evade it indefinitely.

There was no greater terror for the beasts than man. He was the deadly enemy of them all."

Simon hung his head. When the Abbé paused for a moment he asked him, "Then had men only enemies among the animals, and no friend at all?"

"You mean, just as you have a friend in Robot?" asked the Abbé. The boy nodded eagerly. Yes, that was just what they wanted to know. Did a horde of hunters have dogs in those days?

"In the very earliest ages which we know of from cave pictures," said the Abbé, "that is to say, in the middle of the Later Ice Age, which was probably some forty thousand years ago, man was apparently still hunting without helpers. At any rate, there is no hunter with a dog represented in any cave picture. It is only from a later time, long after the ice had melted, that we have pictures which tell us more and give us an insight into the habits and customs of the great hunters.

"In the caves the pictures are almost all of animals, hardly ever of human beings. But in southeast Spain rock pictures have been found which often show human beings. These paintings date from a much later period than the Lascaux ones, and they are not in caves but on exposed niches of rock. Among the figures are as many hunters, also women wearing skirts, and ribbons in their carefully dressed hair, and necklaces made of shells. Frequently the bodies of men and women are painted or dyed. The men wear belts and top boots which are very practical for hunters, and crowns of feathers like the Red Indians. One can see how they dance and hunt, hold courts of justice, and make war on one another. In these pictures there are men leading horses by bridles. But they are no longer the horses with wild flowing manes and narrow slanting eyes which are to be seen in the cave pictures. In the Ice Age man kept neither horses nor cattle nor reindeer. He only hunted them. To kill them was easier than to tame them. But with the taming of animals, friendship between man and beast began. The dog must certainly have been the first friend of man. It was the animal best suited to help him in hunting.

"It is not known for certain from which animal the dog, the first hunting companion of man, is descended. But it was definitely an animal which hunted, and which hunted, moreover, in packs. Otherwise the dog would not even today, after thousands of years, run after something you throw in front of it. Nor would it gobble up its food as greedily as it does, out of fear that another beast would come and snatch it.

"It would seem that there are two animals from which the dog evolved, namely, the common jackal and the wolf. Both lived by hunting, and they hunted in packs like the hunters of the Ice Age. It is quite certain that man never hunted either of them, for there were lots of animals easier to kill whose flesh tasted better. Thus it was that wolves and jackals probably ventured pretty close to the hordes of hunters, to snap up leftovers from the booty. This did not escape the notice of man, who envied these animals their swiftness. He liked these animals to come near him.

He threw the wolf scraps. The wolf, distrustful but hungry, came nearer each time. Doubtless there were some wolves that never came within arrow range of man. These wolves did not like even the scent of man. But there were others that were less wolfish. They were only camp followers, as it were, in the wolf packs, and barely tolerated by their fellow wolves. The packs of two-legged wolves, on the other hand, attracted them.

"And one day it came to pass that a wolf took food from the hand of man for the first time. It trembled as it snapped it. And it fled as soon as it had its teeth in the booty. But it came back. The man knew exactly what he had to do in order to attract the wolf. His eyes penetrated it. He saw what was going on inside the wolf, and he had it 'on a string,' long before he put a collar on it. He took in young wolves that were driven away by the wilder wolves, the animals that sought refuge with him from their worst enemy, hunger. The man shared his food with them. Each time that a wolf ate from the hand of a human being, it paid for the bite by sacrificing a bit of its wolfishness. In the end it was no longer a wolf but a dog, and it never parted from man again.

"It was exactly the same with the common jackal. Man bound both these creatures to himself. He was able to do so. His hands were free; and his brow was not bent to the ground. He caught the animals with his eyes too.

"He, alone of all the creatures that hunted or were hunted, walked upright. Many of the lower creatures

Hunters, stag, and dog from the great hunting scene, Alpera (painted)

tried to stand erect—the caterpillar, the poisonous snake, and the bear, for instance, in moments of rage. But they fell back straightway. Man alone, as long as he was awake, was able to carry his head erect. From his brain went forth those arrows against which no armor was of any avail. For before the hunter sped the arrow from his bowstring, he took aim. And before he took aim, he thought. His thoughts were arrows which never missed their mark. Of these arrows he possessed an endless supply. Thus it was that he became master of the earth. There are many archers," said the Abbé, "painted on the rock shelters of southeast Spain. And there is one of them whom I shall never forget. He is symbolic of them all. He achieves the incredible feat of being supremely in action yet completely in repose. Like a ski jumper in the act of jumping, he is all taut. He himself is the bow from which the arrow speeds . . . an arrow seeking not just the stag or the panther, but soaring over the val-

ABOVE: *Wild horses, Niaux*
BELOW: *Horse's head, Rouffignac (engraved*

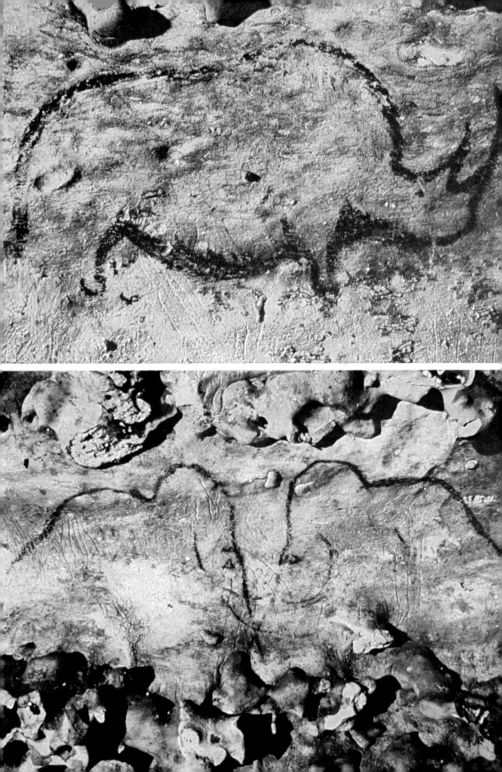

Hunting the wild boar, Cueva Remigia (painted)

ley, over the country which no beast can ever again dispute with him—neither rhino nor bison, neither mammoth nor bear!"

While he was speaking the Abbé had drawn the archer with his finger on the floor of the cave—legs wide apart forming a strong bow, over which the slender body stretched taut. The boys' gaze had followed the Abbé's finger. Now they gazed fascinated at the drawing.

"You remember," said the Abbé, "how it began. A man whose only weapons were his hands and his teeth, in crouching to spring at his prey ducked so low that his fingers touched a stone.

ABOVE: *Rhinoceros, Rouffignac*
BELOW: *Mammoths, Rouffignac*

Hunter pursued by wounded aurochs, Cueva Remigia (painted)

"Thousands of years, probably even tens of thousands of years, went by before the man with the bow and arrow appeared on the scene confronting a bear. No one can say how many generations it took. But finally, there he was. Look at him! With a sure eye he measures his foe. He no longer crouches. He faces the world proudly. He knows: I cannot be beaten so long as I stand erect. Perhaps I will meet with an accident. I may fall on a slippery stone, and the bison, enraged by my harpoon, may take advantage of that. But even so my side will still win. While I draw the bison's eyes on myself, my fellow hunters will do the rest for me and get him down. None of them will be shocked at the sight of me gored by the bison. In death I shall not become a stranger to them. They will lift me up and give me a rock shelter to myself, such as a *living* man has a right to. And the sun will search my face, and when it can find no trace of cowardice in me, the sun will say, 'You have held out, death could take naught from you. Now come home!' "

The Abbé bent down and wiped away the picture with his hand. "I couldn't draw the archer as well as he is painted in the open rock shelter above the Valltorta Gorge," he said quietly. "You must see him some day for yourselves. And he will stay with you as he has stayed with me: you will never forget him!

"It can also be deduced from this picture," the Abbé went on, "that the great hunters believed that

Ibex hunt, Cueva Remigia (painted)

they were given the power to overcome death. Not one of the many cave pictures which have been found up to the present speaks the language of fear. That the people of the Ice Age believed in a life after death is also clear from the fact that they equipped their dead as wanderers who had a long way to go. Food, implements, weapons, and personal adornment were given to the dead for this journey, and red coloring was used to hide the pallor of death. A hearth was erected as a protection against frost, and often, curiously enough, the feet of the dead were bound, obviously lest they should return at night and frighten the living. Sometimes, actually, huts made of skins or branches were erected for the use of the dead."

The Abbé hesitated a little. "Perhaps you will be somewhat surprised at first," he continued, "that the archer is not painted in the same way as the pictures

Wounded archer falling,
Valltorta Gorge (painted)

Archers, Valltorta Gorge (painted)

in your cave. He is of quite a different kind, but he could not be finer. For everything that is not absolutely necessary to show him as an archer has been left out; and everything that makes him an archer is there in perfection. The picture of an archer is a symbol, a formula. It is a letter inscribed in that great book in which are entered the things that survive down the ages; and they are very few. But from the few pictures which have survived one can deduce the era in which they originated."

The Abbé took a flat stone out of his pocket. He let each of the boys take it in his hand and examine it closely. On one side the head of a wild horse was engraved. Only the outline was there, drawn with bold strokes. "This is from the earliest cave-picture period," explained the Abbé. "That period is called the Aurignacian period, after the place Aurignac, where many prehistoric remains of that culture have been excavated. In the Magdalenian period, so named after La Madeleine, the site of many finds in west central France, we get drawings bold in stroke, and big colored pictures. It was only much later, thousands of years after the vast glaciers had melted away, that the hunters began to paint in the taut style in which the archer, for instance, is painted."

The Abbé took the stone back from Simon.

"Later on," he continued, "I will show you other engravings from the different layers, of which several lie over the other in many excavated sites, because the places in question were inhabited for thousands of years. You yourselves will get to know at a glance

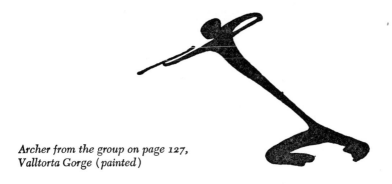

Archer from the group on page 127,
Valltorta Gorge (painted)

the stage of human culture from which a piece of engraved stone or bone comes. In some caves hundreds of stones and bones with sketches scratched on them have been found. And the finished pictures, of which the sketches were the plans, were found later on the walls of caves. This proves that there were real schools in which artists were trained.

"But now let us return to Don Marcelino. In his cave a dumb artist had recovered his power of speech. The pictures had done this. The look in the eye of the bison had so struck the artist that the seal fell from his lips.

"Henry stayed on as a guest in Altamira. He and Don Marcelino often visited the cave, but never again did they mention the newspaper people and the professors. Nor did they speak of the King and the many other people who had visited Altamira. It seemed indeed as if the pictures were to belong forever only to these two men and the girl.

"But meantime, in the depth of his heart, Don Marcelino was reproaching himself all the time. Whenever he was alone he kept asking himself: Why do

129

great scholars keep on searching for traces of early man? Why do they dig and sift the earth? And why are books and articles written about any finds which throw light on the subject? Why do experts from all over the world meet to discuss such matters? Did not the sight of the prehistoric tools and weapons in the glass cases in Paris excite me too? And why? Apparently because it is a great and happy thing to be able to find out how something really was, and perhaps also because there is nothing more important for mankind than to grow in knowledge. And may it not be that these pictures could throw more light on early man, for those who want to learn about him, than any bone or stone implements could? Don Marcelino was in no doubt on this point. Then why do you remain silent? he asked himself. And why do you creep into your cave? Are you perhaps intimidated? Are you frightened?

"Don Marcelino did not let anyone see what was going on in his mind. But his thoughts pursued him even in his dreams. In his dreams he was attacked by animals. A bison made for him. He swung a harpoon and threw himself on the bison, but when he opened his hand there was nothing in it but a blade of straw which blew away. And the bison pushed him aside with its horns. A cave lion sprang up before him. He found that he was carrying an ax, but when he swung it, it turned into a hazelnut in his hand, and the lion came upon him with wide-open jaws. He was not torn to pieces, but he lay there and saw a glacier coming down on him. It did not stop, but rolled over him. It left him

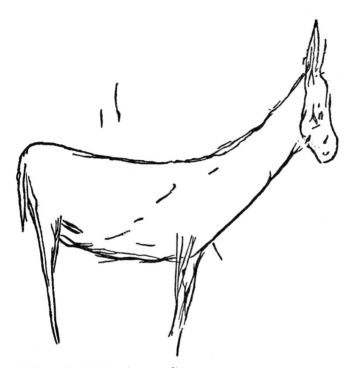

Half-ass, Trois Frères (engraved)

alive, but he could not move and was like a dead man, although he could see out through the ice.

"'Am I really a dead man?' he asked himself as he woke up. 'Have the professors pushed me aside forever, as the bison pushed me in my dream? And will silence roll over the pictures also, like a glacier?'

"One day, when the two men were again together in the cave, Henry asked whether he might copy some of the pictures on big sheets of paper. He was anxious to do his utmost to reproduce the colors as faithfully as possible.

" 'I was just going to ask you if you would,' replied Don Marcelino.

" 'But *you* have the pictures themselves,' said Henry, astonished. 'The cave belongs to you.'

" 'That's just what bothers me,' said Don Marcelino, 'that I and I alone have them. I don't believe it's right. If someone knows something which may be important to a lot of people, is he justified in keeping it to himself?'

" 'But the others had access to the pictures,' said Henry. 'Obviously they did not realize what they were. And the professors, who should have been particularly interested, were invited and didn't come. So why worry?'

" 'The pictures are in danger,' said Don Marcelino. 'As long as the cave was sealed up, they could suffer no damage. But now it's different. Air can get into the cave now. The air is dry today and damp tomorrow, warm by day and cold by night. And that will harm the pictures. For thousands of years the rock has protected the pictures. But now *I'm* responsible for them, because I have widened the entrance to the cave.'

" 'One could close the cave with a big door,' suggested Henry.

" 'I'll do that,' said Don Marcelino. 'The pictures must also be protected against the curiosity of ignorant people. As long as there is no door to protect them, anyone can come in and tamper with them, and wipe off the colors. I will get the door put up without delay. But that is not enough. Something has already been done to the pictures.'

*Warrior horde and stricken man
(so-called Execution picture),
Cueva Remigia (painted)*

"The painter looked up astonished.

" 'Yes,' continued Don Marcelino, 'they have been attacked as fakes. And shall they always be under that suspicion just because I would like to save myself the trouble of another fight? Because I do not have the self-confidence to break through the wall against which Vilanova came to grief? If the pictures are as old as I take them to be, they are among the most important discoveries of all time.'

" 'They *are* genuine,' said the artist. 'I have examined them thoroughly. The technique of the painting in itself points to their great antiquity, precisely because it poses many riddles. It is certain that the great painters of the Ice Age had their technical secrets just as the master builders of the Middle Ages had theirs. Even today, for instance, we cannot put in our stained-glass windows that wonderful red color which is to be found in the windows of the medieval cathedrals. No artist living today could paint the pictures of Altamira. Any doubt about the great antiquity of these pictures is completely unfounded.'

" 'Then I dare not hesitate any longer to fight for them and to force the professors to acknowledge them for what they are,' concluded Don Marcelino.

"The artist no longer offered any objections. He set to work and copied a number of the pictures on stout drawing boards. Then Don Marcelino wrote a book in which he assembled all possible information which could point to the age of the pictures.

"When the professors of France met in Algiers, a city in North Africa, Don Marcelino went there. The professors listened to him, but none of them took him seriously. Don Marcelino then turned to the professors who were holding a congress in Berlin. And he went to Paris too to fight for his pictures. But he made no headway. As soon as he had disposed of one objection, another arose. He met with nothing but mockery and pity. The queer old man from Altamira, they called him . . . the man who won't listen to reason. In the end they actually called him a madman. Nobody listened to him. It was impossible to break through the wall of doubt and prejudice that encompassed him. Even if the whole world thinks I am crazy, thought Don Marcelino, even if they ignore me completely, I will not give up!"

"But he did win in the end, didn't he?" Marcel burst out.

"Yes, he won all right," said the Abbé. He hesitated for a moment, then he added, "But he didn't live to see his victory."

"How could that be?" asked Simon.

"There's something very wonderful in holding out," said the Abbé. "There's something wonderful about persevering in a faith until death. It makes a man mighty even beyond the grave. You will remember that Don Marcelino's hair had gone white in *one* single week. At that time, when the professors did not turn up, he was tempted to take the doubt of others more seriously than his own faith. But then the bison's gaze had such a dramatic effect on the artist Henry that he instantly recovered his power of speech before Don Marcelino's eyes. That day Don Marcelino left the cave with the invincible conviction that he could never be defeated again. Don Marcelino died, but others carried on his work. To this day those others have not forgotten that Don Marcelino was the pioneer."

"And who were those others?" asked Marcel contemptuously.

"I was one of them," said the Abbé, smiling, "and my teacher, Cartailhac, was another. Forty years ago I accompanied him to Altamira. You know, he was that French professor who had raised his voice so vehemently at Lisbon against the 'swindler' of Altamira. But now he set out with me to do penance for his error at the grave of Don Marcelino. Maria of Altamira, by then a young countess, accompanied him on that journey. She closed the castle gate behind us and walked on ahead in silence. In the cave lay the long pick with which she had, many years before, pointed out the dying bison to her father. She bent down and picked it up.

" 'My father worked with this pick until his death,' she said. 'You know that he never gave way to doubt. And what seems more wonderful to me is this: that he was firmly convinced that one day one of his opponents would come here to say, *I was mistaken.*'

"And the daughter of Don Marcelino looked at my teacher without a trace of reproach on her face. 'He has waited for you,' she said solemnly, 'for you or for someone else. And as he knew that there is nothing harder than to admit that the other man is right, he left me directions to pass on this pick as a keepsake to the first of his opponents who would come.'

"Yes, indeed, my lads of Montignac, that's how it was. My teacher too had gone through a difficult time. He had to overcome his own doubts. As he took the pick from Don Marcelino's daughter he was so deeply moved that he could not speak.

"For a while they were silent. They were standing on exactly the same spot where Henry the artist had suddenly found himself able to speak again. The silence was full of meaning. Maria of Altamira understood very well what that silence said. Her father, Don Marcelino, long after his death, was causing it. He had changed his former enemy into an ally. His opponent of yesterday accepted his pick as a weapon with which to fight for the truth, a weapon which came to him from the dead."

"And did the professor still remain silent when he met the other professors who didn't believe in Altamira?" asked Marcel.

"Oh, no!" said the Abbé. "Cartailhac actually published a little book, *The Mea Culpa of a Sceptic,* in which he confessed his error before the whole world."

"How many years after the Lisbon Congress was that?" asked Jim.

"It was twenty-three years later, in 1902," said the Abbé.

The River in the Mountain and the Cat's Hole

"And so ends the story of the discovery of Altamira," continued the Abbé after a pause. "But there was still a great deal to be discovered, above all the mystery which surrounded all cave pictures."

"A mystery?" asked the boys all together.

"Yes," said the Abbé, "a great mystery. The sons of Count Bégouën, who discovered the Trois Frères Cave in 1914, came a big step nearer to its solution. Just think of all that Don Marcelino had to endure during those years of suspicion, when he met with nothing but doubt and mockery; when so many humiliations were heaped upon him that he felt he could no longer breathe freely and often wondered whether he himself would be able to hold out. You can feel all this in the cave of the Three Brothers. There's a long underground passage there which, in many places, is so narrow that one can hardly squeeze through. And in the neighboring cave of Tuc d'Audoubert, which was discovered earlier than the Three Brothers Cave and once was connected with it, there is also a difficult

ABOVE: *Head of an ibex, Rouffignac*
BELOW: *Head of a rhinoceros, Rouffignac*

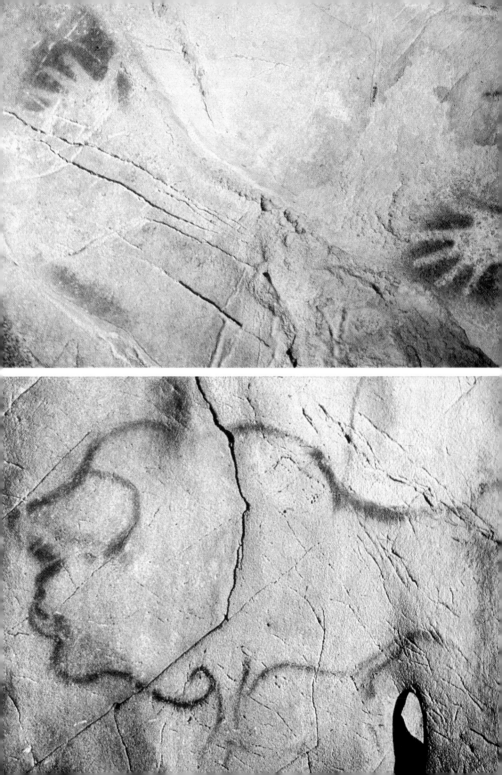

passage. The Count's sons gave it a very apt name. They called it 'The Cat's Hole.' I myself have crawled through the Cat's Hole more than once."

"And what was it like?" asked the four boys.

"It was not very easy," said the Abbé, "and it was especially exciting the first time. But I'd prefer to tell you how the three brothers, and particularly their father the Count, fared the time they discovered the Cat's Hole. That was way back in 1912.

"Tuc d'Audoubert has the most extraordinary entrance of any of the caves. One can only get into that cave by an underground river."

"That would be just right for us," cried Marcel.

"Up to now the Count has only allowed a few scientists to enter the cave," continued the Abbé. "For the first scouting trip the three brothers had built themselves a makeshift boat, which they enlarged into a raft by attaching a few oil barrels to it. On this they penetrated into the mountain until they came to a rock channel which was completely filled by this river, the Volp. The first pictures are there. Dry side-passages lead to halls. There too there are pictures, and lakes—black lakes, which make the silence even deeper. Now and then a drop falls, and after it the stillness is more awe-inspiring than ever."

The Abbé paused a moment. "On the shores of those lakes deep down in the earth," he continued, "the three brothers found the footprints of men who had lived in the Ice Age. They could see the fine lines which a bare foot leaves behind in moist earth just as

ABOVE: *Hands, El Castillo*
BELOW: *Bison, La Pasiega*

a hand does. The lines are as clear today as if the people had been there only yesterday. In the world of caves time becomes meaningless."

"And the Cat's Hole?" Simon interrupted, wide-eyed with curiosity.

"One day when they went back to the cave, the three brothers discovered in the rock a round window which had become overgrown."

"How could that happen," asked Jim, "down in the middle of the earth?"

"That is not so strange as it seems at first glance," said the Abbé. "You know, of course, that the most extraordinary formations are found in limestone caves. The drip from the limestone causes deposits of carbonate of lime to form, which are called stalactites (if they hang) or stalagmites (if they stand). In the Cat's Hole Nature has played the joke of inserting into the narrow passage a bull's-eye windowpane of stalactites. Perhaps it would be more correct to say that in the course of thousands of years she had been closing up the Cat's Hole with bars of this deposit, until at last there were only a few barely visible openings left between the bars. One of the three brothers shone his light on them. A beam lit up the other side. Thereupon the three brothers fetched heavy hammers and sharp picks and smashed the stalactite window. A narrow passage was revealed. The boys were small enough to crawl through it. They discovered new halls, and new pictures, and new footprints. Now, nobody could doubt any longer that these were the traces of people who had lived thousands of years

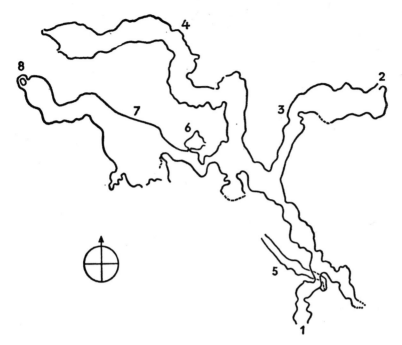

Plan of the Trois Frères Cave: 1. *Original entrance*   2. *Present entrance*
3. *Passage with handprints*   4. *Passage with dots*   5. *Dots and painted*
figures   6. *and* 7. *Scratched drawings of wild cats*   8. *"Sanctuary" (ac-*
cording to Graziosi)

ago. And the pictures that were found by the three
brothers in the halls could also have come only from
these people. The boys ran to their father. The Count
got into the boat with them. Then all four pushed
out from the bank and rowed into the mountain and
crawled as far as the Cat's Hole.

"The Count, who was a brave man, ventured into
it. He was nearly through when he got stuck. He could
move neither back nor forward. One of his sons had

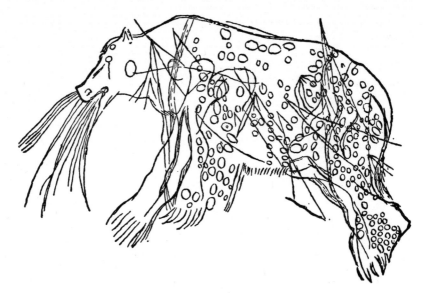

Cave bear riddled with arrows, Trois Frères (engraved)

crawled on ahead. He tried to push his father back, while the others struggled to pull him out. The Count, however, was stuck as firmly as if he himself were a piece of rock. But the thought that he was barring the way out of the cave to one of his sons gave him the strength to force himself through. When at last he got free he was minus his trousers and his shirt was in shreds. The three brothers burst out laughing, and the Count laughed with them, though he did not know how on earth he was to get back through the hole again and into the open. But the three brothers kept hammering away until the Cat's Hole was wide enough for their father. Then they viewed the newly discovered halls, particularly the last chamber. But before

I tell you about that, I want to tell you how the neighboring cave, Trois Frères, was discovered. It is the least accessible of all the picture caves."

"Even more difficult to get into than the Cat's Hole?" asked Marcel.

"Listen and I'll tell you how the discoverer, Louis, his two brothers, and his father fared when they first entered it. It was exactly two years to the day after the discovery of the Cat's Hole. The Count and his three sons had set out to pay a visit to the Tuc d'Audoubert Cave and the Cat's Hole. It was a hot day, July 20, 1914, the second anniversary of the discovery of the cave. They wanted to rest on the way and were looking out for a shady place. There was not a tree to be seen far or wide. Then a peasant told them that there was a 'puffing hole' on the hillside, out of which cool air came.

"The Count listened attentively. When they came to the spot they held their hands into the hole and noticed that the mountain breathed, so to speak. They began at once to widen the hole. It led steeply downward. One of the brothers got a rope. Louis, the Count's youngest son, was the first to be let down—a drop of some sixty feet. As soon as he saw pictures he turned back to the rope and signaled up, and now his brothers, Max and Jacques, came down too. The Count remained behind at the shaft as watchman. His patience was put to a hard test, for it was only after several hours that the boys reappeared. And they did not come through the 'puffing hole,' but came running back to him across the fields, waving from a long way off. 'We have found hundreds of pictures!' cried Louis. And when they had recovered their breath sufficiently, they explained how they had arrived at a new outlet after going through several extremely difficult passages.

"The Count at once hailed a few peasants. These men held the rope, and now the three brothers climbed down for a second time, and with them their father. They came into halls which were like the interior of a cathedral, and then it became difficult to explore farther. In the beginning the passage was not quite so narrow as the Cat's Hole, but it seemed to be endless. In places it was so low that even the boys could not raise their heads and had to wriggle along on their stomachs like lizards.

"As the Count pushed his way forward he suddenly realized that he was about a hundred feet behind his

Two snow owls with young one, Trois Frères (engraved)

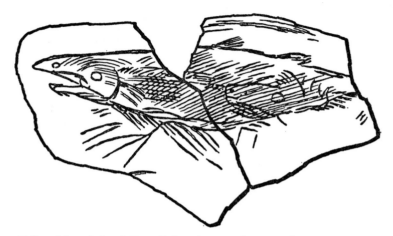

Fish and horse's head, Trois Frères (engraved on stone)

three sons. If he got stuck here, deep down in the earth, there would be no going back. No one could come to his aid. . . . The Count tried to breathe in a way that did not sound like a groan. He did not want to be put to shame by his sons. At last he was through. A high-ceilinged hall opened before him. On its steep walls and in niches of the rocks there were hundreds of pictures—bison, mammoths, wild horses, woolly rhinoceroses, bears, reindeer, hares, fishes, and birds. Louis found two snow owls with a young one up in a place which he reached by leaping from ledge to ledge of rock, yards above the others. And they also found a bear with several holes pierced in its pelt and blood streaming from its mouth.

"The Count looked up. High up, in the mouth of a grotto, above a group of animals, he saw a puzzling figure looking down at him with great dark eyes. This creature had the head of a stag with giant antlers, a long beard which almost covered its breast, bear's paws, and a horse's tail . . . and legs such as only a human being has."

The Montignac boys listened spellbound. In their cave too there was a mysterious animal with human legs, the one with the straight horns. Yet none of them ventured to ask about it now.

"Never in all his life," continued the Abbé, "had the Count felt so forsaken as he did in that long narrow passage. The rocks had encased him on all sides. He could not even raise his head. With the hunters of the Ice Age it had not been otherwise. They too had crawled through the dark narrow passage, through that passage in which there is no more room than in a coffin. . . . But once one is through, one can breathe freely again. Those who had achieved it were received by the mysterious creature with the somber gaze, sur-rounded by innumerable animals. The way back is not so difficult. The exit draws one on, the light of day awaits one outside. And, emerging from the cave, one seems to see the sun for the first time. One has come into the world anew. . . . That is the mystery of the cave of the Three Brothers."

"I'd have been frightened," said Simon.

"Everyone gets frightened," said the Abbé, "for the world of the Ice Age hunters is no longer our world. I was frightened the first time. For down there, hun-dreds of yards from the entrance, there reigns a silence as complete as the silence of the grave. No one can turn back in the narrow passageway. Many narrow passages in caves lead through loose stone, and there are caved-in passages which may once have led to pictures. This is the case in Altamira; and perhaps here in Lascaux also. You yourselves have seen that a big piece has actually fallen off the ceiling of the main hall. So, you see, cave exploring has always been a risky business.

"And once, in the Tuc d'Audoubert Cave, the Count got into a predicament which could scarcely have been worse. One day he had gone with a guest from Germany and entered the cave by the underground river in order to do some digging there. When the two men wanted to return after a few hours the river had risen so high that they could no longer get through. They were cut off from the outside."

"Forever?" asked the boys, alarmed.

"No, only for a night," replied the Abbé.

"It must have been a frightful night," said Jim.

"Whatever did they do the whole night?"

"They made a great discovery that night."

"Did they keep on digging?" asked Marcel.

"Yes, hour after hour," replied the Abbé. "And the visitor found a stone on which a magnificent drawing was engraved. But that was not the great discovery. When the two found themselves shut in they felt frozen stiff with fright. But as soon as they began to dig just as bravely as if they were not shut in there, they got warm and they noticed that their fear disappeared."

The Abbé nodded to the boys.

Sorcerer with animal mask, surrounded by many animals, Trois Frères
(*engraved*)

"To keep on digging was the surest way of driving away fear," he said. "As soon as a fellow stops thinking only of himself, fear no longer has any power over him. The two—the Count and his guest—were practiced cave explorers. Once they had a pick in their hands nothing mattered to them but to keep on digging with watchful eye and hand. The will to discover filled them, so how could even a corner of their hearts remain open for fear to enter? They forgot that during certain times the river closed off the cave for weeks, even for months. Well, the next morning the river fell and the two men brought their finds to light."

"I should like to go through the Cat's Hole some time," announced Marcel.

"I hope you will all do so," said the Abbé. "Down there you will certainly find, like all those who have ventured there before you, that a dark, narrow passage which one has to squeeze through deep down in the earth seems to strip one of fear forever. David, too, experienced that in his cave, and so did the Abbé Lemozi, who crawled through to the two halls of pictures, guided by David."

The Cave of the Bison Dances

"But isn't it all much easier in Altamira?" said George. "For there isn't any Cat's Hole there, or any squeezing through."

"Not nowadays," said the Abbé. "But long ago it was like that in Altamira too."

"Isn't the way into the cave quite easy there?" asked Jim.

"The entrance that the gamekeeper found and that Don Marcelino widened is not the old entrance," declared the Abbé. "The old entrance is choked up. And the hole which you discovered leading into your cave is definitely not the original entrance either."

"And what makes you think that, Monsieur l'Abbé?" asked Marcel.

"Because in the caves where the original entrance still exists the important pictures are never to be found right behind it. One never comes on them straightway. The pictures were always painted in the farthest chambers of caves, or in narrow galleries. Nowadays painters do exactly the opposite. They hang their pictures in halls that are easy to enter and where the greatest

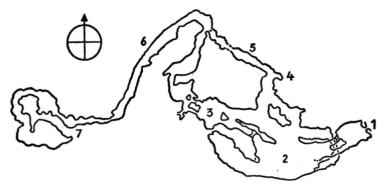

Plan of the El Castillo Cave: *1. Entrance 2. Main hall 3. Hall with bison on stalagmites 4. Signs 5. Gallery of the handprints 6. Gallery of the dots 7. Painted elephants (according to Graziosi)*

possible amount of light falls on them. The painters of the Ice Age hid their pictures."

"Hid them? Why would they do that?" asked the boys.

"Because they wanted to prevent anyone's catching sight of them by chance. Only the hunters, for whom they were meant, were permitted to see them. For that reason they were painted in places which were hard to get at. They are found in chambers which can only be reached if you take a risk such as rowing down a river that disappears deep into a mountain, going through the Cat's Hole, or through a maze of passages out of which you can find your way only with the help of a rope. There's one cave where one has to swim through a lake to get at the pictures. And often even looking at them is very difficult. You have to bend backwards, or crouch into a corner. The pic-

Sorcerer engraved on slate surface, life size, Espélugues, near Lourdes

tures cling to the rock as if they were trying to hide in the hollows."

The boys looked up at the pictures in their cave.

"It must have been very hard to paint up there," said George.

"In the Three Brothers Cave," said the Abbé, "many of the pictures are fifteen feet or more from the ground."

"And how did the artist get up so high?" asked George.

"In many places he could get a foothold on a shelf of rock. Perhaps, too, another man held him up; no one knows exactly," said the Abbé. "But today we know why the prehistoric artists sought out such hidden and inaccessible places for their pictures."

"Why did they do that?" asked the boys.

"Because they were not artists *only*," said the Abbé. "They were something else, too."

"What were they?" the four asked at once, thoroughly excited.

"They were sorcerers," said the Abbé; "sorcerers who painted pictures of animals and sometimes of themselves too. In the cave of the Three Brothers, for instance, in the main hall just behind the long narrow passage, the magician painted himself. And he did it three times, one after another, twice in the midst of the teeming throng of animals, and once high up in the very farthest back niche. The figure with the giant stag's antlers, the bear's paws, and the horse's tail— that's he. Or possibly he may be a god, the god of the animals. At any rate there's something uncanny about

153

him. Time cannot touch him. After thousands of years he still looks down at the visitor with the same somber, piercing gaze with which he once received the hunters of the Ice Age. Most likely it is not a god but a self-portrait of the magician himself. In another place he follows the animals, dancing and playing a flute. It is not so easy to make him and the animals out in a tangle of lines. And the third time he appears dressed in a bison's hide, with an animal mask on his face. He is executing a great dance step, like a bison's leap."

The boys were silent. Their eyes sparkled with excitement.

The Abbé spoke in a low voice, as a man speaks when he is imparting some mysterious information.

"The magician has not left his portrait in every cave," he went on. "Look up there at the 'animal with the straight horns.' Probably that's where the wizard is hiding in here. He has slipped into an animal's hide which hangs down almost to the ground. He has an animal mask on his face. The horns which tower over his head are longer than the horns of any other animal. This is the sign that he has power over all the beasts. Thus, as an animal which rules over all other animals, he dances his dance in an attitude and with the leaps which remind one of an animal."

"Why did he dance like that?" asked Simon.

"Why did he want to look like an animal?" interjected Marcel.

"The people of the Ice Age were hunters, you'll remember," explained the Abbé. "Nothing was more important for them than to find animals which they could

ABOVE: *Black horse, Le Portel*
BELOW: *Three black bison, Le Portel*

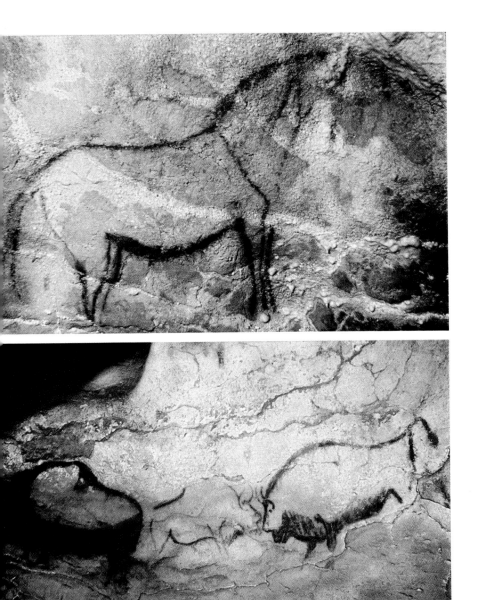

kill. But animals did not always turn up for them before they got hungry. At these times the hunters used to assemble in the cave in which there were animal pictures—those bison, horses, and cattle which the magician of the horde had painted. In the cave they saw the bison just as he stood when ready to attack, or just as he looked when he was dying. And now they hunted these painted animals. The caves populated with paintings of mammoths and bison were places of preparation for the dangers which the hunters met with on the open hunting grounds. They were hunting grounds under the earth. The magician, wearing an animal headdress, danced the magic hunting dance, and the hunters, surrounded by animals, danced like him.

"Even to this day there are hunting tribes who dance before they go out hunting—the Yakuts of Siberia, for instance, and also some Red Indian and Negro tribes. The Eskimos still use magic words like those used no doubt by the sorcerers of the Ice Age, to lure and bewitch musk oxen and caribou. Many words still used in the hunting magic of the Eskimos come from an earlier language which they themselves no longer understand.

"Before setting out on a hunt, the hunters fixed their eyes on the animal which the sorcerer had portrayed on the walls of the cave in colored paints or in line drawings. They aimed at these pictured animals and killed them with harpoons and spears. Deep holes made by shots have been found in the clay models of animals which the magicians had set up. On other animals, again, spears, harpoons, and boomerangs have

ABOVE: *Footprints of Ice Age man, Pech-Merle*
BELOW: *Signs (apparently a hut), La Mouthe*

been found painted, mostly in black or, where a weapon has killed the animal, in red. There are cave pictures of mammoths with a red heart painted on them. While the hunters danced they burned with the desire to hit the heart. They could see the heart before them as a runner on a race track sees the tape while he is still miles away from it. Isn't that the way with you boys too? Don't you always succeed best when you keep your minds fixed on the one thing you want to do, and on nothing else? The hunters of the Ice Age risked their lives at every hunt. Even before the hunt they made a supreme effort to store up in themselves as much presence of mind as they could muster against the moment upon which all would depend. For their hunting dances they slipped into the hides of the animals they had already killed, because they wanted to 'get inside' these animals, to know them inside out, so that when it came to a fight they would aim unerringly at their tenderest spot. That is why, when dancing their hunting dances, they tried to cast off everything which might distract them in the hunt. They forced their way through narrow passages, stripping themselves of everything that could hinder them. They crawled deeper and deeper into the bowels of the earth, in order to emerge from it stronger men, and as if born anew.

"The cave men believed that they could gain from the cave pictures a magic power over the dangerous animals that they met on the open hunting grounds. Only certain special recesses of the caves were reserved as 'sacred' places. For thousands of years the sorcerers, or perhaps their assistants, who were trained artists, painted or engraved the same places. Engraved drawings of a much earlier period have been found under many of the cave paintings of the Later Ice Age.

"During the next few days I will point out to you some pictures in your cave which have earlier paintings under them. Having met with these layers or over-paintings so often in other caves, I noticed them at first glance in yours.

"The picture caves were, in fact, the secret places in which hunting magic was enacted. In the Trois Frères Cave, and also in others, there are so many animals drawn intertwined and merged that one feels almost forced to the conclusion that the magician of the horde conjured up, before the eyes of the assembled horde, the animals they wanted to kill, by carving them out of the rock. There are caves where the rocks on which animals have been carved or painted have been thrown over—the animals have in this way been killed, or drowned in subterranean lakes.

"Only hunters were permitted to enter these caves. No traces of women have ever been found in them. But traces of boys have been found," continued the Abbé after a significant pause; "traces of boys of your age, too.

"Now I will tell you about the very deepest chamber into which the Count and his three sons penetrated after they had passed along the dark river and through the Cat's Hole, and many passages and halls and lakes, and then climbed up a kind of chimney about thirty feet high. This inmost chamber is called the 'Hall of the Bison Dances.' There are only two animals in it, and they are not painted on the wall. They are clay models of a bison bull and a bison cow, and they stand in the middle of the chamber. The magician used to take the sons of the hunters in there before they were received into the tribe of hunters and before they had made their first kill.

"Down there they learned that they themselves had lain hidden in their mothers' womb for nine months before their birth, and that their mothers had borne them in pain. And he told them that they were now to be born anew—as hunters. Down there in that inmost chamber the boys were told of the Great Spirit from whom all life comes forth and to whom all life

Elephant with heart painted on it, Pindal (painted)

*Poisonous spider, the source of arrow-point poison,
surrounded by flies, Gasulla Gorge (painted)*

returns. There they learned that life does not cease
with death.

"At the age of fourteen the boys were initiated into
the mysteries of life and death. They danced the
bison dance. Even to this day one can recognize the
traces of it. They danced with their toes lifted and
stamped their heels as bison stamp their hoofs. In the
glare of the torches held by the sorcerer's assistants
dancing shadows emerged from the wall. In the flicker-
ing torchlight the clay beasts looked as if they were
alive. The boys' bodies glistened; they seemed to
grow as they danced. And after this dance the boys
were considered men. By their initiation they were
made full members of the hunting horde.

"The magician played his flute and the boys stamped
their feet in the rhythm of the dance. Then the magician took the flute from his mouth and sang the in-
cantation or magical chant."

The Abbé stood up.

"Now we'll go down to the lower chamber again," he said.

"Shall we go to the hunter whom the bison has knocked down?" asked Simon.

"The bison has not knocked him down and it can't hurt him," said the Abbé.

"Is the man a sorcerer, then?" asked Marcel.

"Come!" said the Abbé. "Down there in front of the picture I'll try to tell you something more about it."

The Mystery of the Bright Hands

The Abbé went on ahead in silence. The boys too were lost in their own thoughts. Much of what they had heard from the Abbé seemed very puzzling. Yet they did not doubt for one moment that the Abbé must know secret things which were still hidden from them, and that he could introduce them into this secret world of hunting magic.

"Did the magicians of the Ice Age not write down anything—in their caves, I mean?" asked George, as they stood in front of the shaft leading to the lower chamber.

"Nothing of the kind has been found," said the Abbé, "except unintelligible signs—red and black dots. But nobody knows what they mean."

"Are there no words from which anything could be read?"

"No, nothing but pictures and signs. But there's certainly some information hidden in them, perhaps the rules of magic."

For a second time they climbed down into the lower chamber or "crypt" by the rope which Marcel

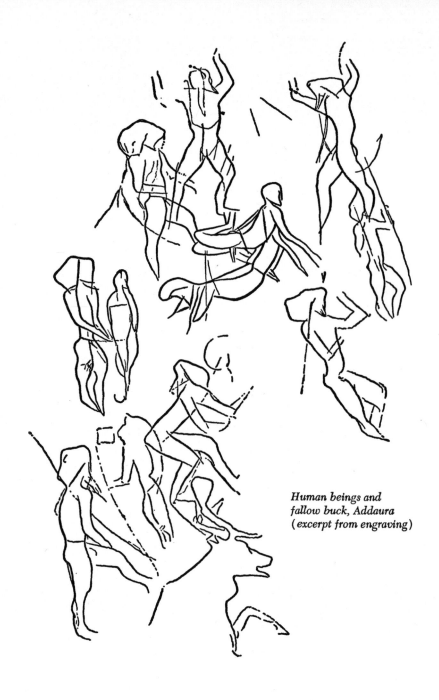

*Human beings and
fallow buck, Addaura
(excerpt from engraving)*

had kept ready. For a long time they looked at the picture—the man lying stretched out, the bird, and the bison. And to the left the woolly rhinoceros with the three horns.

"Those must certainly have been tough customers to fight," remarked Jim.

"Did the rhinoceros kill the man?" asked Marcel.

"It looks as if the rhinoceros and the man had had something to do with each other," answered the Abbé thoughtfully. "One can imagine that powerful beast getting rid of anything that annoyed him. On the other hand, the rhinoceros may well be a picture on its own, just as the pictures crowded together in the main hall are obviously individual pictures, not groups."

"And what about the bird on the pole?" asked Simon.

"The bird is drawn in the same way as the man—just outlined—and both differently from the bison," said Jim.

"Do look more closely at the man's head," the Abbé urged them.

"Why it's a bird's head," exclaimed Marcel. "But how is it that that man has the head of a bird?"

"By means of this picture," said the Abbé, "you will be able to understand all the other pictures better. It is perhaps the most important cave picture that has ever been found anywhere up to the present. It is very difficult, indeed almost impossible, to say for certain what the picture means. Many will take it to represent the death of a hunter. Others will think that is a memorial to a great hunter. Some will believe the man is

Sorcerer with bird mask, Casares (engraved)

dead, and that the curious bird is his soul that has es-
caped from the cage—his body—which has been broken by the bison. But the picture may have yet another
and very much stranger meaning. It may represent an
appeal to the world of the spirit."

The boys looked at the Abbé full of expectation.

"There are still hunters in the world today," continued the Abbé, "who live in just the same way as the hunters of ten thousand years ago. There are also even today regions such as Greenland which are swept winter and summer by the breath of glaciers, the breath of the Great Ice. And certain Siberian, Indian, Australian, and Central African tribes still have their hunting dances in which the dancers in their movements imitate the beasts they desire to kill. These dances seem incredibly wild and grotesque. To an outsider the dancers appear to be quite beside themselves. And that is exactly what they are. They dance themselves into a trance. Their burning desire carries them away, while they are still dancing, on the trail of the beast on which their whole thought is concentrated. In the dance their souls reach the utmost height of tension. Suddenly they let themselves go, as the hunter's hand lets the arrow speed from the taut bow. They fall down. Their bodies lie soulless there, while their souls, which have become arrows (or spears, as in this picture in which the spear has pierced the bison) fly out and strike the beast."

"But surely only a magician can do that?" cried Simon.

"We say 'magician,'" explained the Abbé, "but that is a misleading word. To our minds a magician is a man who makes a watch disappear from the table without moving a finger, or produces a rabbit out of his sleeve. Harmless parlor tricks such as these have nothing in common with what the magician of a hunting horde takes upon himself. With him it is a matter

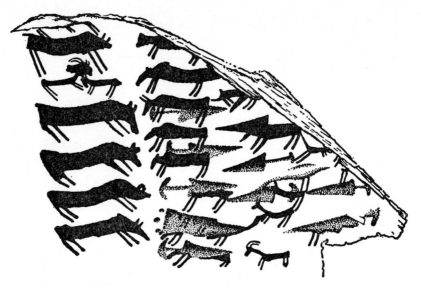

Animals and daggers carved on a rock, Cemmo (Bronze Age)

of life and death. In the cave he really confronts the bison, he believes himself in its presence just as a man believes himself in the presence of God when he prays. With the hunter who is dancing it is the same. He is calling upon the Great Spirit to come to his aid in the hour of supreme danger. And see, this helper has come to the hunter's side in the form of the 'bird on the pole.' Hence, the bird represents the presence of the Great Spirit, but it also symbolizes, no doubt, the utmost awareness or presence of mind on the part of the hunter."

"And is the little bird supposed to be able to help the hunter?" asked Jim, astonished.

"You see, it's not just an ordinary bird," said the Abbé. "It's a *totem*."

"What is a totem?" asked the boys.

"A totem is a guardian spirit," explained the Abbé. "The hunters of the Ice Age—as is apparent from this picture—must have had a belief similar to that of the Red Indians. You probably know the Red Indians only from the books which their pitiless enemies, the white people, wrote about them. These white people came to the country as invaders and hunted down whole tribes of Indians. They changed the Redskin into something which he had never been before.

"Before the white man came the Red Indian was the kind of man who has been depicted for us by Gray Owl and Ohiyesa, who were Indians themselves. We learn from their books that the Redskin was not only a great hunter but also a pious man. He used to mourn for thirty days for the foe who fell by his hand. Every tree, every beast was his brother. He killed animals because he could not help doing so if he did not want to die of hunger. And after every hunt he besought the Great Spirit to give new offspring to the animals to replace the lives he had destroyed. The hunters of the Ice Age did the same. No doubt you have noticed that many of the animals in your cave are heavy with young.

"And just as every Red Indian felt that he was bound in some special way to some animal, so also did every Ice Age hunter. He believed that his personal guardian spirit dwelled in this *one* animal. Among the Red Indians this animal is called the *totem*. The Ice Age hunter too had his totem animal, and he probably also tattooed the picture of his animal on his breast as some Red Indians do.

"In any case this totem picture proves that the hunters of the Ice Age, like the Indians, believed in a Supreme Being—in the Great Spirit. Other proofs of this faith have also been found. In one cave there is a bear made of clay, but only the body with the four paws. The head is the head of a real bear. And the skull was found still lying between the front paws just as the hunters of the Ice Age had laid it—as a sacrifice offered after a successful hunt. The bear's teeth were filed down blunt. This is still the custom among the hunting tribes who live on the edge of the Arctic wastes. They too file down the teeth in the skull of the bear which they offer in sacrifice.

"Hence we see that the hunters of the Ice Age offered sacrifices and prayed in their own way to the Great Spirit. In their worship they were led by the sorcerers, or the medicine men, as they are called among many primitive tribes. These were the 'wise men,' in other words, the priests of the tribe.

"I do not think," said the Abbé very earnestly after a pause, "that we should look down upon these early human beings. In their dances, which were their prayers, they were able to do something which very few people can do in their prayers today. We know that the saints sometimes have ecstasies when they pray— they are carried outside of themselves. In this state of ecstasy they see the Crucified Lord; they hear voices.

Human hand and red spots,
Pech-Merle (painted)

We know that the Maid of Orleans was called by such voices to save France. Saul, persecutor of the Christians, was turned into Paul the Apostle after he had been blinded by a light from heaven on the road to Damascus. True, the hunters of the Ice Age did not yet have the revealed religion which has been given to us. But the Great Spirit was present among them when they prayed in the depths of the earth, in the caves which were their sanctuaries."

"Were these caves, then, to the hunters what churches are to us?" asked Marcel.

"No one could put it better than that," said the Abbé, and his eyes shone with pleasure. "That is the secret of the cave of Altamira, and that is the secret of all those caves in which there are pictures dating from the Ice Age."

The Abbé led the boys' eyes on to the pictures once more. "The bird is the most insignificant thing up there," he said, "yet it draws one's eyes. More power goes out from it than from the bison. The bird will never again leave the hunter's side. When the hunter awakes from the trance of ecstasy into which he has fallen during the magic dance, he will go forth to the hunt no longer armed only with a spear. His totem will accompany him henceforth. Then, when he confronts a bison, his presence of mind will not fail. The 'bird on the pole' will tell him what he has to do in the decisive moment."

The Abbé gazed in front of him, deep in thought. "There may be even more to be read in this picture," he continued. "Perhaps we shall be better able to solve its meaning when we find other similar pictures."

The Abbé noticed that Simon had become pale with excitement. "Now let's climb out," he said. Looking up at the steep wall of rock, he added, "I hope you'll help me!"

Marcel, being the most expert, was the first to climb up out of the shaft. It was not difficult, with the help of the rope, to get the other boys up, and then they all joined forces to haul up the Abbé. As they passed back through the cave, the boys cast only a fleeting glance at the pictures. They had become aware that many hours must have passed, and they were hungry for food, but still more for light.

But the Abbé stopped once more just in front of the exit. "There's one more thing I must tell you about," he said, "before we leave your cave. You will remember how young David from Cabrerets discovered the Pech-Merle Cave all on his own under great difficulties. Besides the pictures David saw something which touched him strangely—the imprint of human hands which stood out palely against a red or black background. These bright hands are to be seen in other caves too, and in the Gargas Cave hands with a finger missing have been found. . . . It is known to us today that the man who laid his hand against the rock and blew color over it had sacrificed the missing finger. Right up to our own day such sacrifices are practiced by many primitive races. Someone who escapes from great danger offers a bit of himself in sacrifice. In David's cave and in many other caves, including Altamira, the hunter laid his hand on the rock and blew color over it, so that the impression of the outspread hand remained there. Or he dipped his hand in paint and pressed it against the rock. This hand of the hunter said, 'Look, Great Spirit, I have come here to thank you for my good luck in the hunt. Please stand by me in the future also!' These brightly colored hands," concluded the Abbé, "are a proof that the great hunters lifted up their hands now and then in petition to a Helper who they believed had power over all things and was present everywhere, even in the rocky depths of the earth."

The Abbé looked up once more at the ponies. "I've never seen anything lovelier than those in any cave," he said.

"It was I who saw the ponies first," said Simon, "and I like them best too."

"They're wonderful," said the Abbé. "And now it's time for us to leave the cave."

Stepping Out into Sunshine

Marcel crawled cheerfully up toward the stones with which the exit was blocked. But to push the stones aside was not quite so easy. Marcel tried several times with both hands. All of a sudden they moved quite easily. They just tumbled away, and when Marcel stuck out his head, his dazzled, blinking eyes caught sight of two legs moving hastily aside. And the voice of Simon's teacher said, "You seemed to be trying to push me right down to Montignac!"

"Have you been sitting here all the time?" asked Marcel, astonished.

"Almost an hour," confessed Mr. Laval. "I just couldn't stand waiting at home. . . . Aren't you hungry?"

"We're frightfully hungry," said Marcel, "but in there we didn't notice that we were."

The rest of them crawled one after the other into the open. Simon was the last. He took his time. As he wormed his way to the exit he saw something magnificent. The sun was standing in exactly the spot toward which he was crawling. It hurt his eyes, but he kept looking up at it all the same. He was crawling right into the sun.

The trunks of the trees were red with the radiance of the sunset. Half the sky was shining with a fiery glow. The boys and the Abbé from Paris pressed their eyelids together. They squinted until their eyes looked like those of the wild horses.

But the last light of day did not hurt their eyes for long. Soon they were no longer blinded by the light. And suddenly Simon cried, "Here comes Robot!" He had left the dog at home so that he would not disturb the Abbé. But he had broken loose and had picked up their scent. The boys ran to meet him.

"These four boys have discovered the most beautiful cave in France," said the Abbé to the teacher. "It is probably indeed the most magnificent cave in the whole world. The Lascaux Cave pictures are at least as well preserved and as vivid as the great Altamira pictures. And here in Lascaux there is not only *one* hall. One gallery leads to another, and many of the pictures are masterpieces. The most carefully made copies which will be printed later in books will only give a vague conception of their beauty. Many of them are so impressive that, having once looked at them, you can never forget them."

"And nevertheless," admitted the teacher, "I did not see the pictures yesterday at the first glance. It was only after a while that they emerged, as it were, from the rock. But then they seemed to stand out so distinctly, so clearly, that I cannot understand at all how it was possible even for a moment not to have seen them. Isn't that most extraordinary?"

"Many an expert noted for his sharp-sightedness has had the same experience as you," the Abbé assured the teacher. "And many have actually worked for years excavating in painted caves and noticed nothing. Indeed it seems," he concluded, "as if the eyes of us grown-up people were obscured at times—blind to just the most significant things. Is it not remarkable that the most important painted caves of the Ice Age have been discovered by boys, and that the little girl of Altamira was only a child of nine when she was struck by the glance of the bison's eye?"

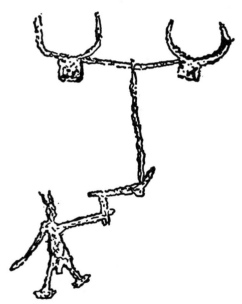

Plowman with team of oxen, Monte Bego Cave. The heads and horns of the oxen are foreshortened. This picture belongs to the Bronze Age. The roaming hunter has turned by now into the peasant tilling the soil

The Abbé from Paris and the teacher from Montignac hurried on to catch up with the young discoverers, around whom Robot was dancing wildly.

Epilogue

And now, thank you, Marcel and Jim. The two of you led me through your cave and made me feel at home there. You, Marcel, I thank particularly, because you even climbed with me down to the "Crypt," which is so difficult of access. As we crouched before the "bird on the pole" you told me of that wonderful day of the discovery just as calmly and quietly as though there were no automobiles and buses on the way to Lascaux. While you were doing so Jim kept watch outside just as he had the time that you and Simon and Simon's teacher were down in the cave. I shall never forget that, Marcel. All the same, I cannot dedicate this little book only to you and your three companions; nor only to the great Abbé from Paris. David, too, has a claim, and Gaston; and above all, the girl from Altamira.

And what about Simon? I don't mean Simon, the youngest of you four; I mean Simon of Altamira, the seventy-two-year-old, who crawled before me into the farthest nook of "his" cave, pouring out an enthusiastic torrent of words in four languages as he pointed to the engravings.

And old Clastres of Niaux, who, with his hazel switch, called my attention to each puddle; and old Justó of Pindal, his house surrounded by myrtles and fig trees, who has turned the little piece of ground in front of "his" cave into a bit of paradise, a fairy meadow hidden in the rocks fifty feet above the Bay of Biscay.

And Felipe! How could I ever forget how he guided me through the labyrinthian passages of La Pasiega and El Castillo; and how, after we came to know each other, he took me, though still a little hesitantly, to the cave of Las Monedas, which he had discovered himself only shortly before and which had not yet been really explored at all!

And Count Bégouën who, in 1914, as the fifteen-year-old Louis, penetrated into the passages of Trois Frères. I recall how, as we stood in that rarely visited cave, he pointed out to me with a smile the shaky folding chair on which the great Abbé always sat while he copied the pictures. . . .

I must include all of them in my greeting to you, Marcel and Jim. I owe it in part to all of them, too, that this little book about "the discovery of the boys from Montignac" has come into being.

Appendix to the New Edition

The Lascaux photographs were kindly placed at my disposal by Professor Dr. E. Pietsch, Director of the Gmelin Institute in the Max Planck Society. The other color photographs for the new edition of the book were made in the course of a long cave tour which I made, together with Lissy and Hannes Burges, into the Franco-Cantabrian regions and the rock shelter—the *Abris*—of eastern Spain.

In the *Abris* we found only very poor remnants of pictures. The unprotected rock walls, open to all comers and much abused by the destructive "water method"—the spraying of the stone to make the pictures more visible—will very soon be robbed of the last traces of color if they are not fenced off.

Both in southern France and in Spain we met with the utmost helpfulness and courtesy. We are particularly indebted to the owners of the caves of Rouffignac and Le Portel, the Plassard family and M. Vezian, for their hospitable reception. Our thanks are also due to the cave guides of La Mouthe, Cap Blanc, Le Grèze, Les Combarelles, Font-de-Gaume, and Pech-Merle, as well as to M. Peyrony, the curator of the museum of Les Eyzies, where we were allowed unrestricted opportunities to work.

For me it was a chance to meet once again Jacques Marsal in Lascaux, Simon in Altamira, old Justó in Pindal, Felipe Puente in El Castillo, and M. Clastres, Junior, in Niaux. We were guided at the Valltorta Gorge and the Gasulla Gorge by Domingo Jondarello, who had acted as guide and companion to Professor Hugo Obermaier in the early days of prehistoric cave exploration, and was himself the discoverer of several painted rock shelters.

For many valuable suggestions and for the reading and checking of the book I am indebted to the late Abbé Henri Breuil, to Professor Herbert Kühn, and to H. G. Bandi.

The following books also helped me greatly:

H. Breuil, *Four Hundred Centuries of Cave Art*, Montignac, 1925.
H. G. Bandi and J. Maringer, *Die Kunst der Eiszeit*, Basel, 1952.
H. Kühn, *Die Felsbilder Europas*, Stuttgart, 1952.
P. Graziosi, *Die Kunst der Altsteinzeit*, Stuttgart, 1958.
Bandi, Breuil, Berger-Kirchner, Lhote, Holm, Lommel: *Die Steinzeit*, Baden-Baden, 1960.

Europe at the Time of the Great Glaciation
(according to Bandi-Maringer, *Die Kunst der Eiszeit*)

The cave pictures of the Franco-Cantabrian area came into being toward the end of the last Ice Age, the Würm Age. Modern methods, for instance, the examination of radioactive particles of charcoal present in organic remains and the examination of glacial deposits, show that the Altamira pictures are a good

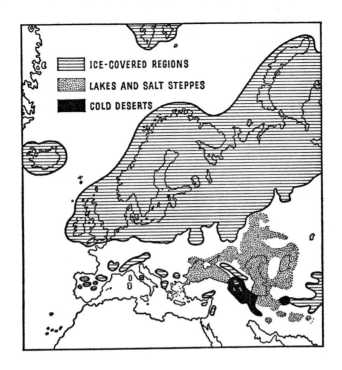

ICE-COVERED REGIONS
LAKES AND SALT STEPPES
COLD DESERTS

fifteen thousand years old. A more exact dating is not possible up to the present.

On the edges of the Great Ice a form of existence which might be described as a higher form of hunter's life developed. The hunters, or hunter hordes, had to cope day after day with animals, the hunting of which meant a life-and-death struggle. As the ice receded and the dangerous animals—the mammoth, the woolly rhinoceros, the cave lion, and the cave bear— became extinct, man's power to create animal pictures also decreased. The pictures on the rock shelters of eastern and southern Spain, which are of considerably later date, are not nearly as fine on the whole as the Ice Age cave pictures. By this time man was no longer living in the midst of perpetual ice. He no longer had to risk his life day after day in the struggle for existence. By then, he could breed cattle and till the soil. In these later pictures human beings play a far greater role than the animal.

Some Caves and Other Sites of Ice Age and Later Ice Age Art

IN FRANCE:

1 *Teyjat*
2 *Les Combarelles*
3 *Lascaux*
4 *Pair-non-Pair*
5 *Le Gabillou*
6 *Limeuil*
7 *Font-de-Gaume*
8 *La Mouthe*
9 *Pech-Merle (Cabrerets)*
10 *Ebbou*
11 *Baume-Latrone*
12 *Espélugues*
13 *Labastide*
14 *Marsoulas*
15 *Les Trois Frères*
16 *Bédeilhac*
17 *Niaux*
A *La Colombière*
B *Rouffignac*

C *Fourneau du Diable*
D *La Grèze*
E *Cougnac*
F *Gargas*
G *Le Portel*

IN SPAIN:

18 *Pindal*
19 *Altamira*
20 *El Castillo Chimeneas La Pasiega Las Monedas*
21 *Covalanas*
22 *Los Casares*
23 *Amarga*
24 *Gasulla Gorge*
25 *Valltorta Gorge*
26 *Araña*

27 *Alpera*
28 *Cogul*
H *La Peña de Candamo*
I *Tormón*

IN ITALY:

29 *Levanzo*
30 *Addaura*
31 *Romanelli Monte Cemmo and Monte Bego, farther north, near the Lake of Garda (not shown on map)*

IN GERMANY:

Klause bei Neuessing, Bayern

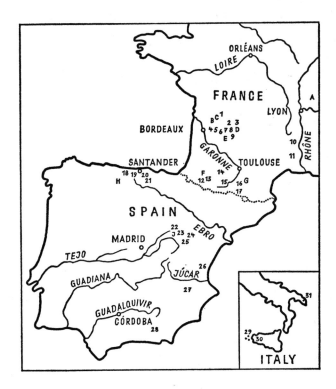

Picture Caves Discovered by Girls and Boys:

Altamira (1879) by Maria de Sautuola.

La Mouthe (1895) by Gaston Bertoumeyrou and three other boys, who forced their way into the difficult passages which were blocked with clay.

Tuc d'Audoubert (1912) and *Les Trois Frères* (1914) by the sons of Count Bégouën.

Pech-Merle (1920) by the boy David of Cabrerets, who forced his way, after many attempts, through to the halls containing the pictures.

Lascaux (1940), by the four boys Ravidat, Marsal, Agnel, and Coencas.

Baume-Latrone (1940), by three schoolboys, Suter, Rogue, and Martin, from Nîmes.

Sallèles-Cabardès, also called *Gazel* (1947), by children.

It could be that even more picture caves were actually discovered by children, but the archaeologists who later excavated these caves and made their results known were given credit for being the real discoverers. In the case of many caves, discovery and personal history have been closely connected. For instance, the cave of Cueto de Lledias surrendered the secret of its pictures to a man who had hidden in it during the Spanish Civil War.